Reading for Interest

Merry Hearts

and Bold

CALIFORNIA STATE SERIES

PUBLISHED BY
CALIFORNIA STATE DEPARTMENT OF EDUCATION
Sacramento 1954

REVISED EDITION

The stories and poems in this book were selected by

BARBARA NOLEN

and illustrated by

FRITZ KREDEL

Educational Consultants

PAUL WITTY *and* PHYLLIS FENNER

Copyright, 1942, 1950, by D. C. Heath and Company

printed in
CALIFORNIA STATE PRINTING OFFICE
SACRAMENTO 2ND PRINT, 60M 1956

Reading for Interest

PAUL WITTY, *of Northwestern University, has served as consultant for this series, co-operating with the educators whose names appear beneath the titles listed below.*

Ned and Nancy, by Inez Hogan. Illustrated by Corinne Malvern.
KATE KELLY, State Teachers College, Castleton, Vermont

Bigger and Bigger, by Inez Hogan. Illustrated by the author.
KATE KELLY, State Teachers College, Castleton, Vermont

Little Lost Dog, by Lula Wright. Illustrated by Winifred Bromhall.
KATE KELLY, State Teachers College, Castleton, Vermont

Molly, Pete, and Ginger, by Esther Phillips. Illustrated by Ottilie Foy.
ESTHER PHILLIPS, Public Schools, Montgomery County, Maryland

A Home for Sandy, by Romney Gay. Illustrated by the author.
LULA WRIGHT, Horace Mann–Lincoln School, New York City

Rain and Shine, by Ardra Soule Wavle. Illustrated by Ruth Steed.
ETHEL MABIE FALK, Author and Lecturer, Madison, Wisconsin

Something Different, by Eva Knox Evans. Illustrated by Pelagie Doane.
ETTA ROSE BAILEY, Matthew Maury School, Richmond, Virginia

Lost and Found, by Robin Palmer. Illustrated by Edna Potter.
RUTH BRISTOL, Muskingum College, New Concord, Ohio

Secrets and Surprises, by Irmengarde Eberle. Illustrated by Helen Sewell.
MARGARET L. WHITE, formerly Directing Supervisor, Public Schools, Cleveland, Ohio

Fun and Frolic, Barbara Nolen, Editor. Illustrated by Emma Brock.
FLORENCE BRUMBAUGH, Hunter College Elementary School, New York City

Do and Dare, Barbara Nolen, Editor. Illustrated by Richard Floethe.

Luck and Pluck, Barbara Nolen, Editor. Illustrated by Decie Merwin.
DOROTHY K. CADWALLADER, Carroll Robbins School, Trenton, New Jersey

Merry Hearts and Bold, Barbara Nolen, Editor. Illustrated by Fritz Kredel.
PHYLLIS FENNER, Public Schools, Manhasset, New York

The Brave and Free, Barbara Nolen, Editor. Illustrated by Harve Stein.
URSULA BRINGHURST, New York University, New York City

CONTENTS

A MERRY HEART

GOOD SPORTS

Animals Can Be Heroes

Facing Danger

Mighty Magic

BOYS WHO FOUND OUT

SIGHTS AND SOUNDS

FESTIVAL TIME

A MERRY HEART

CHING–LING

PLAYING JOKES

CHING-LING could never decide what there was about Silk and Satin Lane that made this street much the nicest in Shaohing. It wasn't fine houses, for the lane was crowded with little shops, each one open to the street so that anyone could look inside. It wasn't gardens, for in the whole street there were no more flowers than could be planted in earthen jars. It wasn't beautiful clothes; except for the flowered jackets of the children, there was nothing but faded blue cotton.

Ching-ling lived with her Uncle Sing, the wood carver, on Silk and Satin Lane. One day, as she sat on the front step of the shop and watched him polish a chest, she asked him why it was the nicest street in the whole city.

Uncle Sing said it was the people — the gay, fun-loving people who sat in their doorways while they worked and called back and forth across the narrow street to their neighbors.

How they loved a joke! Everyone on the street had gathered around when the three Wong boys next door had sent Ching-ling a box wrapped in fine red paper and tied with a silk cord. When she opened it there had been nothing but a handful of goose-down that blew away in the wind.

And everyone in the street had laughed about the rice cakes Ching-ling baked for the Wong boys, using salt instead of sugar.

Ching-ling always had fun when she visited the Wong family. The father and the three boys were acrobats, and when they practiced in their kitchen they taught Ching-ling and her brother how to do stunts with them. They said Ching-ling was almost as good as a boy, although sometimes her pigtails got in the way.

One evening the three Wong boys came home quite breathless with excitement. They had been with their father to the home of the Magistrate, where they had performed stunts for his little daughter.

"She was just your age, Ching-ling," they said. "We told her about you. She kept asking us questions."

"Did she?" cried Ching-ling, her eyes shining with excitement.

"Such a house you never saw," said Wong, the father. "There are courtyards with lotus lily pools. Inside the house are chairs of carved teakwood, and screens of embroidered silk!"

"There is a spirit wall at the front gate with a great dragon painted on it," cried the eldest boy.

"And kitchen maids running here and there with trays of tea and sweet cakes," said Wong.

Ching-ling's eyes opened wide. "Please, may I go with you the next time?" she begged. "Remember, once I was in your show and I didn't make one mistake."

Uncle Sing pulled her ear. "Indeed, she was always a tomboy," he said to Neighbor Wong, "and no one knows that better than yourself."

Wong laughed and said, "I would rather have her than the Magistrate's pale daughter who is the same age."

That evening, while Ching-ling set the table with the gray-green cups for tea and the blue-green bowls for rice, and her pretty young aunt lighted the red candles, there came a knocking at the front of the wood carver's shop.

Ching-ling pulled aside the curtain that separated their

big kitchen from the shop and saw her brother take from a messenger a letter bound with a red cord.

"What is it?" she cried excitedly.

Uncle Sing pulled out his glasses and carefully hooked them behind his ears.

"Well, now, it is for Ching-ling," he said.

Ching-ling dropped the chopsticks in surprise.

"It's from the Magistrate," said Uncle Sing. "He asks that you spend the day with his daughter."

Ching-ling gasped in surprise.

"Did you hear that, Elder Brother?" she called into the shop, where her brother was putting away his wood-carving tools.

"It is most unusual," said Elder Brother.

"The Wongs told her about me," said Ching-ling. "She is just my age."

"And why should she not invite Ching-ling?" asked her aunt, as she stirred the rice on the stove. "It will be good for both of them."

"Well," said Uncle Sing, "it is written very properly and on fine paper, too."

"Still, it is a strange thing," said Elder Brother.

Ching-ling's aunt poured the rice into a big bowl in the center of the table and pulled up four benches. "Be sure to take notice of everything in the Magistrate's house," she said.

Although Ching-ling sat at the table with the others and dipped into the bowl of rice and bean sprouts, she quite forgot to eat. Elder Brother had to remind her that unless she ate she could hardly walk all the way across the city to the Magistrate's house.

"Walk!" exclaimed Uncle Sing. "They are to send a boat for her. She is to wait on the steps where Fish Bridge Street crosses the canal at the Hour of the Snake in the morning."

Ching-ling almost burst with excitement. Long after Uncle Sing and his wife had drawn the curtains of their big bed and Elder Brother had gone to sleep in the shop, Ching-ling was busy about the room. She heated water in the iron kettle, took a bath by the fire in the big square stove, and brushed oil into her two pigtails before she tied them with blue cord. Then she hung up the plum-colored silk jacket and the pale blue trousers that her aunt had made from some of her own clothes and went to bed.

GOING ON A VISIT

Everyone in Silk and Satin Lane knew about the letter early the next morning. Ching-ling herself had told them. And when at last the Hour of the Snake came, she danced off to the bridge that crossed the canal to wait for the Magistrate's boat.

7

First she sat on the stone steps that led from the street to the canal. Then she climbed up and leaned over the railing at the very highest part of the curved bridge where the boatman would be sure to see her. Once in a while a silk-canopied boat came down the canal among the farmers' scows. Each time, Ching-ling ran to the steps expecting it to stop for her and each time it went skimming by. When the Hour of the Snake had passed, Ching-ling decided that perhaps the boatman had missed her. Well, then, she would walk.

The street beside the canal was roughly paved and there was always the danger of having her jacket splashed with water by an awkward boatman. She chose instead the Street-of-Big-Shops. For the first time in her life she hurried past the fine silk shops and the shops where fans were sold. Today she had no time to waste and, besides, she must be careful to keep her silk slippers out of the gutter that ran in the middle of the narrow street.

At last she came to the tall spirit wall that stood before the gate of the Magistrate's house. There was the great dragon painted on it just as the eldest Wong boy had said. She smoothed her jacket and skipped past the wall to the gatehouse.

"Good day," said the old gateman, bowing hastily, as he stepped from the door of his gatehouse and came toward her.

8

"Good day," said Ching-ling. "I have come to visit the Magistrate's daughter."

The gateman looked surprised.

"Your sedan chair is outside?" he asked politely.

"Oh, no, I walked," said Ching-ling.

The gateman hesitated. Small daughters of the Magistrate's friends always came by sedan chair or by boat. Never since he could remember had a visitor just walked in by herself. But Ching-ling looked so sure of her welcome that at last he brought a chair for her and asked her to sit down. Then he went across the courtyard to a one-story house, where he whispered to some men servants standing at the door.

When he came back he brought a tall man in a long white coat, who bowed and asked Ching-ling to follow him.

Down a winding passage they went and across three courtyards. In each one, stiff little trees and peony bushes in china pots stood on the stone paving. In the third one they stopped while the man in the long white coat whispered to a group of women servants.

Ching-ling pulled the letter from a pocket inside her jacket, and handed it to the man. He pretended that he could read but she noticed that he handed it to one of the women. She looked quite puzzled as she read it aloud to the others.

"I didn't wait for the boat," explained Ching-ling. "I thought the boatman had missed me."

The man pulled a low bench under a tree and asked her to sit down and wait.

"There must be some mistake," he said politely, as he disappeared with the letter.

Ching-ling could see the serving maids peeping into the courtyard. At every door there were laughing eyes looking at her.

She wondered why they were laughing. Was there something strange about her? To be sure, she wore a jacket and trousers instead of the long straight dress that was in fashion, but hers were made of silk brocade. She was very proud of them, for they were the first things she had ever owned that were not made of faded blue cotton. And her shoes matched the plum-colored silk of her jacket. Her aunt had made them for her.

Suddenly she heard someone whisper, " — not even invited." Ching-ling was speechless with horror.

Not invited! She understood the laughter now. This must be another joke. The Wong boys were getting even with her for the rice cakes made of salt. Of course they had gone to the letter writer who sat under a blue umbrella on the corner. Many times Ching-ling had seen him writing letters for those who could not write themselves.

Her face grew crimson as she thought of them laughing. She thought of the whole of Silk and Satin Lane laughing, for she had boasted to everyone in the street that she was invited to the Magistrate's house. Not once had she guessed that the letter was a joke.

She would have given anything she owned — even her plum-colored jacket and the shoes that matched — if she could have run away from the Magistrate's house without being seen. She jumped up, but in her excitement she couldn't remember through which of the doors she had come. All of the buildings looked alike. She darted through a doorway and across a room, only to find herself in another courtyard. There was a garden with a lily pool and three willow trees.

Through the round moon-gate in the wall at the far side ran a little girl and after her hobbled her nurse on tiny bound feet.

SURPRISES

"She came to call on me," said the girl. "Indeed I will see her."

Ching-ling turned to run, but the girl had seen her and called to her to stop. She was so embarrassed she hardly dared look up.

"I do not want to stay," said Ching-ling. "It was a joke."

"Oh, tell me," cried La-mei.

So Ching-ling told her about the Wong family and about the rice cakes made of salt and about the letter tied with a crimson cord.

The eyes of the nurse twinkled as she took Ching-ling by the hand and led her through the moon-gate into the garden that belonged to La-mei.

"The juggler's boys told me about you," said La-mei.

12

"You can turn handsprings and stand on your head," she added.

"Those things I did as a child," said Ching-ling, for she felt the nurse would not think well of them.

"I wish I could do as you do," said La-mei.

Then, while the kitchen maids set a table by the lily pool in the garden and brought out bowls of chicken and rice and some nut cakes, Ching-ling told La-mei about her home in Silk and Satin Lane. She told about the wood carver's shop, and about the big room behind it where the light from the fire in the cook stove danced on the polished sides of the bed. She told about her brother, who was her uncle's helper and was learning to be a wood carver himself. He had made her a chest with a big round lock for her very own.

She told about her friend, the jade merchant, who wore all his jade on cords about his body to keep the colors warm and bright. She told about the Chens across the street, who let her carry their baby in a sling on her back if she was very careful not to jump around.

"Silk and Satin Lane must be wonderful," cried La-mei, her eyes shining with wonder.

When they had finished drinking their tea, La-mei showed Ching-ling the things her father brought her when he came home from his travels. There was a Manchu doll from Peiping and a foreign doll from Hong Kong.

The foreign doll had blue eyes and curly yellow hair. It looked very strange to Ching-ling, but not nearly so strange as the shoes with wheels that he had brought from Shanghai. La-mei was afraid to put them on.

Ching-ling tied them on her feet and tried to skate over the rough paving in the courtyard. To be sure, she sat down heavily several times, but in no time at all she could make them go where she wished.

The nurse ran to call the three little boys who were La-mei's cousins and their nurses to come and watch Ching-ling skate. After them came their mothers and soon the garden was filled with people watching Ching-ling fly over the rough stone walks on her shoes with wheels.

Before she knew it, the sun was going down behind the garden wall, and Ching-ling remembered that she must go home.

When La-mei insisted that she take the roller skates home, Ching-ling could hardly speak for surprise.

"Come often, come often," begged the three little boys.

The nurse smiled as she put down her sewing, clapped her hands for a maid servant, and ordered a sedan chair to take Ching-ling home. And then she asked whether Ching-ling's uncle would let her come again.

"I would rather go to Silk and Satin Lane," said La-mei.

To Ching-ling's delight the nurse said that perhaps this could be arranged.

"Go slowly, go slowly," said La-mei, bowing politely.

Ching-ling climbed into the sedan chair, waved good-by, and pulled the curtain down before her face. She knew that was the proper thing to do when one rode in a sedan chair, although she couldn't see much through the tiny window as she went down the street.

"Make way, make way," cried the men who carried the chair on their shoulders, and the crowds scattered before them.

It was not until they passed the tea house with the wind bells under the eaves and turned into Silk and Satin Lane that Ching-ling remembered the letter and the Wong boys' joke. Of course, it didn't matter now, but when she saw the three Wong boys sitting on their front step eating their evening rice, she could not help raising the curtain of her chair and bowing to them very politely.

Their mouths fell open in surprise.

"Ching-ling!" cried Elder Brother, coming out of the shop when he saw the sedan chair. "Where have you been?"

"I've been to the Magistrate's house," said Ching-ling.

"But the letter was just a joke," said Elder Brother.

"I know," said Ching-ling. And she held up the roller skates as she stepped out of the sedan chair. "See what La-mei gave me," she said.

In a moment the street was filled with people laughing until they held their sides. But it was not Ching-ling at whom they laughed.

Little by little, Silk and Satin Lane grew quiet again. By the time Ching-ling sat down to eat her supper with her family as usual by the light of the tall red candles, she was sure she must have dreamed it all. But there was Elder Brother smiling proudly at her, and there on the shelf above the kitchen stove were two funny shoes with wheels.

Esther Wood

BELLS IN THE NIGHT

WHAT TIME IS IT?

"MY DEAR," said the King of Dunsoon to the Queen, "I think I have a chill."

The Queen looked up from her needlework and said, "A chill? Then off to bed you go."

"But I am not a bit sleepy. It may not be anything. Besides, I have important work to do."

The Queen opened her eyes wide and exclaimed, "Not sleepy! May not be anything! Important work to do! The very idea! Do you think for one moment that I am going to let you go about with a chill that may lead to a cold that may lead to a fever that may end in your death? You may be the King, but please remember that I am the Queen."

"But, my dear, it is only — " began the King. Then he sneezed. That settled it.

The King went to bed with a hot-water bottle at his feet, a mustard plaster on his chest, three extra blankets to cover him, and four cups of hot lemonade to drink.

"Now, do try to sleep," urged the Queen. "It will do you a world of good."

The King slept for two hours. "Strange!" he thought, when he woke. "My chill is gone. I feel as well as ever!"

The King ordered a bath. He had himself dressed and then went about his business of being a king.

That night, when the King went to bed at his usual time, he could not fall asleep. He lay on his right side. He lay on his left side. He turned over and lay flat on his back. He twisted, rolled, turned, tossed, bent, and unbent to no purpose. He just was not sleepy.

At last he gave up trying to sleep and lay with his eyes wide open, staring into the darkness. He thought of this. He thought of that. Mostly he thought, "Why, oh, why did I go to sleep in the middle of the day?"

Somewhere in Dunsoon a clock struck the hour.

The King counted the strokes. "H'm — eleven. It must be eleven o'clock." (Which was not bad reasoning even for a king.)

Then, as if it had politely waited for the first clock to finish, a second clock in another part of Dunsoon began to strike. Again the King counted up to eleven. A third clock and then a fourth clock followed, until all the clocks in Dunsoon had struck the hour. When the night was quiet once more, the King said, "It must be eleven o'clock."

After a long, long while, all the clocks struck again — just once this time. "H'm," thought the King, "it must be half-past eleven."

After a long, long, long while, the clocks again began to strike. The King lay awake and counted. "It must be twelve o'clock," he said into the darkness. There really was no doubt in the King's mind that it was twelve o'clock. Yet, to make certain, or perhaps because it gave him something to do, he reached under his pillow and pulled out his great gold watch and chain. He turned the watch this way and that way until it caught the bit of soft moonlight that was in his room and he could see that it was twelve o'clock. In fact, it was five minutes past twelve o'clock.

The King put his head down on the pillow and tried to sleep. Instead of falling asleep he was more wide awake than ever. His mind went round and round like a merry-go-round. Thoughts hopped on and off again in the strangest fashion. Sometimes the merry-go-round was just crowded with thoughts. At other times it was altogether empty.

All at once so strange a thought hopped on that the King sat upright in bed and exclaimed, "Now, let me get this straight! When a clock strikes one, it is one o'clock or half-past some o'clock. When a clock strikes eleven times, it is eleven o'clock. But is it eleven o'clock at the first stroke or the last stroke? Or is it eleven o'clock at the sixth stroke, which is the middle stroke?"

It did not seem to make sense at all.

"And here's another thing. If it is eleven o'clock at the first stroke of the first clock, then all the other clocks are not telling the truth. The idea of any clocks in my kingdom not telling the truth! I won't have it. I'll have to do something about this. I'll — um — ah — um," the King yawned. The King yawned so great a yawn that his head fell back and back until it touched the pillow, and the King was fast asleep.

The King did not wake up until the sun was shining. He sat up in bed, stretched this way and that, and yawned again. As he was doing this, a clock began to strike. The King stopped right in the middle of a most refreshing yawn.

"Those clocks!" he remembered. "I'll have to see to them today."

Everyone knows that kings do not see to clocks. It takes a clockmaker to do that. (That is, if one wants it to run again.) What the King really meant was that he was going to order somebody to look into the matter and find out why it was that all the clocks did not strike at the same time.

The King spoke about the difficulty to his chief adviser. The chief adviser whispered a word or two to the head of the Privy Council. He took the matter up with the oldest clerk, who gave an order to the youngest clerk. The youngest clerk sharpened a fresh quill and wrote out a proclamation on a large sheet of parchment. It was handsomely dressed up with flourishes and fancy capitals. It was the loveliest piece of writing that had ever been seen in Dunsoon.

The oldest clerk picked it up, looked at it this way and that, gave a growl of disapproval, and said to the youngest clerk, "Humph! I did better than that when I was first here."

When the King saw it, he gave a chuckle of delight. "This will do it!" he said. "It is just the thing." He read it over three or four times. With each reading he liked it better. He read it yet a fifth time. " 'Be it known by these presents that all bell-ringers, bell-pullers, and clock-strikers are commanded to appear on Tuesday next, between the hours of ten and high noon, in the great hall of the Palace, on pain of displeasing His Royal Highness, the King of Dunsoon.' Yes, I like it," ended the King, and he gave it to a messenger to declare to the people of Dunsoon.

The Queen Decides

It was not every day that a meeting was called in the great hall of the Palace of Dunsoon. The curiosity of those invited was so great that they began to arrive long before the appointed time. They were dressed in their best clothes. They sat on the stiff court benches feeling hot, worried, and uncomfortable. When a person is called to the presence of his king, he wonders what he has done and imagines the worst. Each one asked himself, "Can it be that the King has found out about — " "Did I forget to — " "I wish that I had — " without getting much in the way of satisfaction.

At ten minutes to noon by the King's watch, the King

came into the great hall. The people stood up and awaited his pleasure. All the King did was to ask them to sit down and listen. They did.

Some listened by closing their eyes. Others cupped a hand behind an ear. Another turned his one good ear toward the King and screwed his face into a thousand wrinkles. They all listened for one, two, five, nine minutes. Still they heard nothing unusual.

A fly came in through the open window and made a buzzing sound. Was that what they were supposed to hear? The Queen and some of her attendants were chattering lightly in the next room. Could that be it? It sounded very pretty. The distant moo of a cow came in to them and still there was no sign from the King. All the small noises of Dunsoon drifted in, around, and out again, and still the people in the courtroom waited.

The King pulled out his great gold watch and chain from his pocket, glanced at it, put it back, arose, and said, "Clock-strikers, bell-pullers, and bell-ringers of Dunsoon! You have been invited here to take up a very serious matter. What time is it?"

At this question every person who had a watch took it out. Those who had no watches tried to look at the watch of a neighbor. Each one called out the time his watch showed.

"Two minutes to noon."

"Two minutes past noon."

"Just noon."

"Five minutes to noon."

"My watch has stopped."

This led to a great comparing of watches, with no one willing to accept anyone else's watch as being correct.

"Well," broke in the King, "what time is it?"

"About noon, Your Majesty," someone offered.

"Very well, then. Listen!"

Again the court became strangely silent. It became so

quiet that each one fancied that he could hear his watch ticking. Or was it his heart?

A bell began to strike the noon hour with great, solemn bongs. Over in a far corner a little bit of a man smiled to himself as he recognized his bell. He was the oldest bell-ringer in Dunsoon. He nodded his head in time to the bongs and looked around, as if to say, "Do you hear that? That is my bell!"

One by one the clocks struck, each in its special way — long, slow, unhurried bongs; short, high, quick clings; booming, shattering, rolling clangs; and soft, tinkling chimes. Finally, each clock and chime had done its work.

In the silence that followed, the King spoke again. "Did you notice anything?"

"Very pretty!" said one.

"Just on time!" said another.

"The same as it has always been!" from a third.

"If you please! If you please!" interrupted the King. "Will someone kindly tell me what clocks are for?"

"To tell the time, of course, Your Majesty," he was assured.

"Is a clock doing its proper work if it is not telling the right time?"

"Oh, no, Your Majesty!"

"Then, if a clock is supposed to tell the right time, how is it that each clock strikes at a different time?"

The people looked at one another. They had never thought about clocks that way. But someone had to answer the question, as it would not have been polite to let the King wait forever.

At last the little bit of a man spoke up and said, "O King! It may be that I can explain it. I am the oldest bell-ringer in Dunsoon. It is understood that because of my many years of service, my bell should be the first to sound the hours and half-hours. On sunny days there is the sun-dial in the city square to tell us heavenly time. We set our clocks and watches by it. On cloudy days I trust to my watch. It gains about two minutes every twenty-four hours, but I allow for that. I check it the next day the sun shines. When my bell rings, we among ourselves are agreed that it sets the hour. Then each of the others follows in order. For years it has been this way in Dunsoon. Your father and his father before him liked it that way. We hope it pleases you, too."

"It does not please me. It is not businesslike. One bell striking the hour in Dunsoon should be enough. However, I do not want to put the other bell-ringers out of work."

"What does Your Majesty suggest?"

"All the bells, chimes, gongs, and clocks will have to strike the hour at one and the same time. It is to begin at midnight this very night. I have spoken!"

A king had spoken. There was nothing to do but obey.

That night the King went to bed earlier than he usually did. He was very tired because of the day's great work. The extra meeting about the clocks had been a strain.

Little by little, the whole town of Dunsoon fell asleep. Here, a light was put out and a window barred. There, a door was shut against the night. A soft "good night" was heard blowing through the night air. A little sigh went whispering among the houses. A young dog barked once, but his voice sounded so strange in the quiet night that he put his tail between his legs and ran off to his doghouse. The keeper of the watch walked his rounds, calling, "All's well! Sleep! All's well in Dunsoon!"

The night grew soft and still. Dunsoon lay wrapped in a blanket of quiet sleep. Then it happened!

Without a word of warning, without the slightest notice, there was a great, ear-splitting crash. It seemed as if a whole summer's thunder had been let loose at one time. Dunsoon rocked to its very base. Was this an earthquake? Had something exploded? Had the world come to an end?

Windows went up. Heads came out. People rushed into the streets in their night-clothes. Children — and grown folks — who remembered that they had forgotten to say their prayers said them hurriedly.

The King himself was thrown out of bed. He lay on the floor and wondered what had happened. Should he call out the army? Should he summon his council? Instead, he called the Queen, who was already running to him to find out what was happening.

The first crash was followed by another equally great. Ten more thunderous, frightening, ear-splitting crashes followed one another. Then all was strangely still except for the echoes rolling and rebounding in the far-off hills. Dunsoon once more went back to the quiet of the night.

Dunsoon did, but not the people of Dunsoon. They wanted an explanation of this unusual happening. They hurried through the streets. They met at the corners and whispered to one another. Finally they gathered in the palace courtyard. The murmur of their voices floated up to the King's open window.

The Queen suggested, "See what the people want!"

The King wrapped a robe around himself and stepped out on the balcony. When he saw the crowd gathered there, he spoke to them thus: "Friends! People of Dunsoon! Some great disaster has come to Dunsoon. Do not

be afraid. Dunsoon still stands. With the dawn, we will take counsel, learn what danger threatens us, and do our best to overcome it. Go to your homes. Sleep, if you can. I, your King, will watch and take thought for you. But wait! I see a messenger approaching."

The crowd waited. The messenger stood in the middle of the courtyard and spoke to the King in a clear, loud voice, "Your Majesty! The bell-ringers of Dunsoon greet you. They hope that you are pleased now with the clocks of Dunsoon."

A cry of relief went up from the people. "Why, the noise was only the clocks striking all at once!" they cried.

The King swallowed hard, ran his fingers through his hair, and said, "Well, well!"

The Queen said, "You and your clocks! If I have any-thing to say about it — and I do — you'll order the bells to be struck as they were before and always have been. I would like to have a little peace. Bells in the night! Hm-m! Bells in your head! Let's go in and get some sleep!"

J. Linwood Cutler

29

TOM TWIST

Tom Twist was a wonderful fellow,
  No boy was so nimble and strong;
He could turn ten somersaults backward,
  And stand on his head all day long;
No wrestling, or leaping, or running,
  This tough little urchin could tire;
His muscles were all gutta-percha,
  And his sinews bundles of wire.

Tom Twist liked the life of a sailor,
  So off, with a hop and a skip,
He went to a Nantucket captain,
  Who took him on board of his ship.
The vessel was crowded with seamen,
  Young, old, stout and slim, short and tall,
But in climbing and swinging and jumping,
  Tom Twist was ahead of them all.

He could scamper all through the rigging,
  As spry and as still as a cat,
While as for a jump from the maintop
  To deck, he thought nothing of that;
He danced at the end of the yard-arm,
  Slept sound in the bend of a sail,
And hung by his legs from the bowsprit,
  When the wind was blowing a gale.

The vessel went down in a tempest,
  A thousand fathoms or more,
But Tom Twist dived under the breakers,
  And, swimming five miles, got ashore;
The shore was a cannibal island,
  The natives were hungry enough,
But they felt of Tommy all over,
  And found him entirely too tough.

So they put him into a boy-coop,
  Just to fatten him up, you see,
But Tommy crept out, very slyly,
  And climbed to the top of a tree;
The tree was the nest of a condor,
  A bird with prodigious big wings,
Who lived upon boa-constrictors,
  And other digestible things.

The condor flew home in the evening,
  And there lay friend Tommy, so snug,
She thought she had pounced on a very
  Remarkable species of bug;
She soon woke him up with her pecking,
  But Tommy gave one of his springs,
And leaped on the back of the condor,
  Between her long neck and her wings.

The condor tried plunging and pitching,
  But Tommy held on with firm hand;
Then off, with a scream, flew the condor,
  Over forest and ocean and land;
By and by she got tired of her burden,
  And when she flew close to the ground,
Tom untwisted his legs from the creature,
  And quickly slipped off with a bound.

He landed all right and feet foremost,
  A little confused by his fall,
And then ascertained he had lighted
  On top of the great Chinese Wall;
He walked to the City of Pekin
  Where he made the Chinamen grin;
He turned ten somersaults backward,
  And they made him a mandarin!

Then Tom had to play the Celestial,
  And to dangle a long pigtail,
And he dined on puppies and kittens,
  Till his spirits began to fail;
Then he sighed for his native country,
  How he longed for its ham and eggs!
But in turning somersaults backwards
  His pigtail would catch in his legs.

He sailed for his dear home and harbor,
  To the house of his mother he flew,
He climbed up the lightning-rod quickly,
  And came down the chimney flue.
His mother in slumber lay dreaming
  She never would see him more;
Then she opened her eyes and Tommy
  Stood there on the bedroom floor!

Her nightcap flew off in amazement,
  Her hair stood on end with surprise;
"What kind of a ghost or a spirit
  Is this that I see with my eyes?"
"I am your most dutiful Tommy —"
  "I will not believe it," she said,
"Till you turn ten somersaults backwards,
  And stand half an hour on your head."

"That thing I will do, dearest Mother."
　　At once, with a skip and a hop,
He turned the ten somersaults backwards,
　　But then was unable to stop!
The tenth took him out of the window,
　　His mother jumped from her bed,
To see his twentieth somersault
　　Take him over the kitchen shed.

Then over the patch of potatoes,
　　And beyond the church on the hill,
She saw him tumbling and turning,
　　Turning and tumbling still;
Until Tommy's body diminished
　　In size to the head of a pin,
Spinning away in the distance,
　　Where it still continues to spin.

William Allen Butler

HOW THE MANX CAT
LOST ITS TAIL

FAR, far away in the Irish Sea there is a tiny island called the Isle of Man, where the cats have no tails to wave when they are angry, or to curl round them when they sit down. These cats are called Manx cats.

Although Manx cats are just as handsome as other cats, they look different because they have no tails and because their hind legs are longer than the legs of ordinary cats. With these long hind legs they can hop like a rabbit when they are in a hurry. Their silky fur may be black, white, gray, or striped, but the very best Manx cat has stripes of three colors, black, white, and amber.

No one really knows how the Manx cats lost their tails. It happened many hundreds of years ago when people were not paying much attention to such trifles. But the Manx people who know most about it say that this is the way it happened.

At the time when Noah was calling all the animals into the Ark, there was one Manx cat that was out hunting mice. Sure enough, it had a lovely striped coat of three colors, black, white, and amber. Noah was eager to have

35

this cat on board his Ark because a cat of three colors is supposed to bring good luck.

It had taken Noah, his wife, and their three sons many years to get all the animals together in the Ark. They had worked hard arranging the animals in their places and keeping them friendly. Shem, the first son, who was three hundred years old, had complete charge of all the birds of the air. Ham, the second son, who was two hundred and fifty years old, had complete charge of all the fishes of the sea. And Japheth, the third son, who was only two hundred years old, had complete charge of all the animals of the forest and jungle.

Noah's wife was a good housekeeper and knew just how to take care of children's pets. She had complete charge of all the pet dogs, cats, ponies, birds, goldfish, and every other kind of pet animal you can imagine. For, you remember, Noah took every kind of living creature into the Ark.

After Noah discovered that the Manx cat was the only animal not yet in the Ark, he took upon himself the task of calling it in. He stood at the door of the Ark all of ten years calling "Kitty, kitty, kitty, kitty" until he was worn out. Who would not be worn out if he was six hundred years old and had been calling "Kitty" for ten years?

One day, Noah was about to give up. His thin legs simply would not hold him up any longer, and so he slid down by the door of the Ark. There he sat stroking his long white whiskers. He must have been there a month or more when up came Shem, his first son, greatly excited.

The birds had heard Noah calling the cat, and they were all perched on the roof ready to fly away. So Shem came to Noah to find out what to do. But when Shem saw Noah, he said, "Why, Father Noah, whatever is the matter with you? In all these three hundred years I have never seen you so tired and nervous."

"Quite so," said Noah to his first son. "The Manx cat does not come when I call her. The sky is getting darker and darker. I am afraid the rain will fall any minute, and I shall have to close the door before the cat gets in."

"Let me try," said Shem, and he called "Kitty, kitty, kitty, kitty" for a month or so. But no cat appeared.

By this time some of the fish had heard about the cat, and so all the little fish hid themselves behind the whales and sea-lions. This worried Ham, the second son, so that he came running to Noah to find out what to do. As soon as Ham saw Noah, he said, "Why, Father Noah, whatever is the matter with you? In all these two hundred and fifty years I have never seen you so tired and nervous."

"Quite so," said Noah to his second son. "The Manx cat does not come when I call her. The sky is getting darker and darker. I am afraid the rain will begin to fall any minute, and I shall have to close the door before the cat gets in."

"Let me try," said Ham, and he called "Kitty, kitty, kitty, kitty" as loud as his two-hundred-and-fifty-year-old voice would permit. But no cat came.

It does not take rats and mice very long to get the news that there is a cat anywhere near. The minute the word reached them, they all locked themselves up in the elephant's trunk. This worried Japheth, the third son, so that he ran to Noah to find out what to do. But when Japheth saw Noah, he said, "Why, Father Noah, whatever is the matter with you? In all these two hundred years I have never seen you so tired and nervous."

"Quite so," said Noah to his third son. "The Manx cat

does not come when I call her. The sky is getting darker and darker. I am afraid the rain will fall any minute, and I shall have to close the door before the cat gets in."

"Let me try," said Japheth, and he called "Kitty, kitty, kitty, kitty" as loud as his two-hundred-year-old voice would permit. Still there was no sign of the cat.

While Japheth was calling the cat, the mice had wiggled around in the elephant's trunk and tickled it so that the elephant was running wild all over the Ark. When it got to the side where the hippopotamus was, the Ark almost tipped over.

Noah's wife could not stand having things out of order. When the Ark almost tipped over, she ran to Noah to find out what to do. When she saw him she said, "Why, Father Noah, whatever is the matter? In all these four hundred years I have never seen you so tired and nervous."

"Quite so, dear wife," said Noah. "The Manx cat does not come when I call her. The sky is getting darker and darker. I am afraid the rain will begin to fall any minute, and I shall have to close the door before the cat gets in."

"Well, I'll try," said his wife, and this is the way she called the Manx cat: "Spss, pss, pss, pss." She must have been a Manx housewife, for she knew just how they call cats on the Isle of Man.

No sooner had she finished than the rain began to fall. Noah called his sons to help him close the heavy door of

39

the Ark. He called sharply, "Who's out is out, and who's in is in," and slam went the door.

As soon as the cat had heard Noah's wife call "Spss" it came running as fast as it could. Half drowned by the rain, it just squeezed in as the heavy door closed, but not in time to save its tail. That was cut off.

For a long time, no one on the Ark noticed the cat. It had crept off into a corner, feeling very sad over losing its tail. This was the most painful experience it had ever had and it hardly knew what to do or where to go. But it had learned this lesson — that it never pays to wait till the last minute.

Then, one happy day, Noah's wife found the cat. She took it to the fire to dry and bandaged with great care the place where the tail had been.

The first time the cat walked about to see how well it could balance itself without any tail, it met Father Noah.

"What a queer look Father Noah is giving me!" thought the cat. "I guess he does not know how I sneaked in, and how he cut off my tail with that heavy door. I'll speak to him about it." So she said:

"Bee-bo, bend-it, my tail's mended.
I'll go back to Man as soon as I can
And get copper nails to mend it."

But it was some time before the cat could start back to the Isle of Man, for the flood lasted forty long days and forty nights. Then the Ark came to rest on the top of a mountain. The rain stopped. The waters went down and at last the heavy door of the Ark was opened. The cat, you may be sure, was the first animal to go out. It started straight for the Isle of Man, and kept looking for its lost tail all the way. But no tail was to be found. After the cat reached the tiny island in the Irish Sea, it kept on hunting —

Up to the top of Snaefel Mountain
Down to the bottom of the deepest glen;
All along the rocky shore,
And then all over again.

Of course, by this time, the tail had probably been washed away in the flood. Or it may be that, if the cat found its tail, there were no copper nails to mend it.

All we know is this: although hundreds of years have passed since then, today you will find hundreds of cats without any tails living their nine lives on the Isle of Man.

Blanche Cowley Young

THE PLAINT OF THE CAMEL

Canary-birds feed on sugar and seed,
   Parrots have crackers to crunch;
And, as for the poodles, they tell me the noodles
   Have chickens and cream for their lunch.
      But there's never a question
      About *my* digestion —
   Anything does for me!

Cats, you're aware, can repose in a chair,
   Chickens can roost upon rails;
Puppies are able to sleep in a stable,
   And oysters can slumber in pails.
      But no one supposes
      A poor Camel dozes —
   Any place does for me!

Lambs are inclosed where it's never exposed,
   Coops are constructed for hens;
Kittens are treated to houses well heated,
   And pigs are protected by pens.
      But a Camel comes handy
      Wherever it's sandy —
   Anywhere does for me!

People would laugh if you rode a giraffe,
  Or mounted the back of an ox;
It's nobody's habit to ride on a rabbit,
  Or try to bestraddle a fox.
    But as for a Camel, he's
    Ridden by families —
Any load does for me!

A snake is as round as a hole in the ground,
  And weasels are wavy and sleek;
And no alligator could ever be straighter
  Than lizards that live in a creek.
    But a Camel's all lumpy
    And bumpy and humpy —
Any shape does for me!

Charles Edward Carryl

FOUR ARROWS

Long ago the great warrior, Tamerlane, came down from the Mongolian plains and conquered the land that is now Turkey. There he found pleasure in the comradeship of Nasr-ed-Din Hodja. Often Tamerlane grew tired of his bowing courtiers who always said, "Yes, my lord."

The Hodja was different. Here was a man who treated peasant and emperor alike. Here was a man who did not weigh every word before he let it reach his emperor's ears. Being with the Hodja was to Tamerlane like a fresh breeze from the mountains.

It was a sunny spring day when Tamerlane asked Nasr-ed-Din Hodja to go with him to the plain where his soldiers were at their archery practice. The Hodja had been planning to plant onions that day, but he needed no urging to put off that back-breaking job till another day.

It was the sort of bright, sunshiny day when a man feels twice as strong and clever as on a dark day. With each step across the fields to the place where the soldiers were practicing, Nasr-ed-Din Hodja felt younger and braver and more sure of himself. By the time they joined the soldiers, he was no longer the old man at whom all the people in the village loved to laugh because of his foolishness. He was, instead, Tamerlane's fearless companion, a man who could do anything.

"A good shot that," said the Hodja, as a soldier's arrow pierced the bull's-eye of the target. "It reminds me of the way I used to handle a bow and arrow."

"Really?" Tamerlane looked at the Hodja in surprise. "I had never heard that you were an archer."

"Oh, yes, indeed! I was once a famous archer." On a day like this, the Hodja could imagine anything. "I remember how men used to come from distant cities to see me shoot. Indeed, my hands itch for the feel of the bow again."

No sooner was that wish out of the Hodja's mouth than Tamerlane signaled to a soldier.

"My soldiers need to see some good shooting," he said to the Hodja, as he took the soldier's bow and arrow. "Here is your chance to show us how it really should be done." Tamerlane held the bow and arrow toward Nasr-ed-Din Hodja.

"Oh, you must not rob your soldier of his chance to practice!" The Hodja was thinking faster than he had thought in many months. "He needs it more than I do."

"Watching your skill will more than make up for the time he loses." Tamerlane still held the bow and arrow toward the Hodja.

"It is so long since I have worked at archery," protested Nasr-ed-Din Hodja. "It might be better not to do it today."

"Oh, it will come back to you as soon as you feel the good strong bow in your hands." Tamerlane set the arrow in place, pulled back the cord, and sent the arrow whizzing within two hairs of the bull's-eye. "See! It is months since I have touched bow and arrow, but I feel as though I had been shooting yesterday."

"Perhaps I should wait until this cut on my finger is well." The Hodja tried to shift the interest from archery to a little scratch on one finger.

"That finger does not have to touch either bow or arrow," Tamerlane continued firmly.

"You forget the pain in my shoulder which has been bothering me all winter," suggested the Hodja, grasping for any excuse.

"You said this morning that today's spring sunshine

46

had cured that pain." Tamerlane held the bow and arrow firmly toward the Hodja.

Nasr-ed-Din Hodja knew a command when he saw it — and a command from Tamerlane was a command indeed.

"Oh, of course!" The Hodja tried to wear an air of confidence as he took the big bow in his hands. As a matter of fact, he had never held a bow and arrow before. A quick glance at a soldier at target practice showed him which way to hold it. After two or three nervous attempts, he managed to fit the arrow into something near the right position. He squinted painfully at the target, pulled back the cord, and shut his eyes as the arrow fell limply to the ground just a few inches from his feet.

Tamerlane expected to see the Hodja angry or embarrassed. Not at all! The old jaunty grin suddenly spread over his face.

"That," said the Hodja, "is to show you how your Chief Huntsman shoots."

Nasr-ed-Din Hodja took another arrow from the soldier's quiver. He beamed pleasantly at the little group of soldiers that was fast gathering about him and Tamerlane. Perhaps he had made a foolish boast, but he trusted to his wits to get him out of a tight hole.

For the second time, the Hodja put his arrow in place. This time he gave a mighty pull on the string and sent the arrow whizzing high into the air. Half a dozen soldiers jumped aside so that it hit no one as it fell to the ground not far from its starting place.

"And that," said the Hodja with a cheerful nod, "is to show you how your Governor shoots."

Nasr-ed-Din Hodja took a third arrow and fitted it to the bow. The soldiers drew back, ready to dodge in any direction. It was well that they did, for the third arrow went far to the right of the target.

"And that," said the Hodja smiling, "is to show you how your General shoots."

Nasr-ed-Din Hodja took a fourth arrow. He no longer bothered to squint at the target. He simply put the arrow to the cord, gave a jerk, and let it go where it would. This time the arrow whizzed straight between the rows of grinning soldiers, and lodged neatly in the exact center of the bull's-eye.

For a minute, the Hodja stared with open mouth and popping eyes at his arrow quivering in the bull's-eye.

Then he smiled once more with all his usual confidence. The Hodja might be a foolish fellow but he knew how to act wise when fortune favored him.

"And that," said he, as calmly as you please, "is to show you how Nasr-ed-Din Hodja shoots."

Tamerlane, who was not called "the Great" without reason, smiled pleasantly and kept his own counsel.

Alice Geer Kelsey

MERRY TYLL, THE JESTER

LET me tell you about Merry Tyll. They call him Tyll Ulenspiegel in Flanders and other names in other lands, but I like Tyll best of all because it is a simple name and fits him as long ears fit the hare.

I want to tell you these stories because they have been told to boys and girls in every corner of the Old World for hundreds of years, and now the time has come to tell them to boys and girls in every corner of the New World as well. And I want to tell them to you because they are such grand stories. They are full of laughter, which destroys cruelty, and they are full of adventure, which keeps the world ever young.

Five hundred years ago, Merry Tyll, the Jester, wandered around Europe, from one place to another. He went from Saxony to Denmark and then back to Germany. He went from Berlin to Prague, and from Prague over the Alps to Rome, seeking the springtime. And everywhere he went, he made merry.

50

Staff in hand and pack on back, Tyll wandered through Germany and came to Brunswick. The sharp March wind tried to go through his very body, and Tyll tried just as hard to find shelter to protect it. It was a close race between the two.

One day he was in the inn where the bakers came to gossip. There he met a master baker who was known as a joker. Tyll looked so sad that the baker thought he would have some sport. He told Tyll he looked like a monkey dragged from the mud, and asked whether his business was teaching songs to the owls.

"No," replied Tyll, "I was helper to a baker who liked to sleep behind the oven."

"Well, I am not lazy, but I need a baker in my shop."

So the bargain was closed, and Tyll went to the baker's home, where he was sheltered from wind and weather.

Soon Tyll found that the baker planned to put all the hard work on him, while spending his own nights at the inn. The very second night his new master said to him, "You will do all the baking in the night and I will help you in the morning."

Now, as Tyll knew, most of the baking was done during the night. But he replied innocently, "What shall I bake, good master?"

This made the baker angry. "You are a baker," he replied, "and ask me what to bake? Ho, ho, ho! What did you bake before? I suppose big-eyed owls and long-tailed monkeys. Well, try the same here. Try it here, my smart fellow!" He walked out, laughing.

Tyll laughed, too, and began to work. He took the dough and shaped it into fat owls and thin owls, tall owls and short owls. He made dough monkeys with long tails and short faces, and some with long faces and short tails. In short, instead of rolls and bread and cake, he made over a hundred monkeys and owls of every shape and size.

These he baked brown and crisp. Just as he was taking them out of the oven, about the time when gray cats come home, the baker came in. He stopped where he stood.

"Fool! Have you lost your mind? What have you done? Where are the white rolls, the little breads and cakes which you were supposed to bake?"

"I baked exactly what you ordered me to bake. Didn't you tell me to make big-eyed owls and long-tailed monkeys? That's exactly what I did."

"O fool of fools! What shall I do with these? I can't sell them. Now you will have to pay for that dough or I'll put you in prison."

"I'll pay for the dough," Tyll replied, "but then these dough-animals belong to me."

"Take these owls and monkeys who look like you and give them to those who are your brothers."

Tyll paid the money, took them, and went to the market-place. It was the day before St. Nicholas Day, and he thought it would be easy to sell the funny-looking rolls and cakes to the children.

He was not wrong. A great crowd came around to look at the baked monkeys and owls. Soon he had a good trade, selling his strangely shaped cakes at a much higher price than he could have sold those of ordinary shape.

When the baker passed and saw what he saw, he cried, "Now you will have to pay me for the wood and the hire of the oven."

"A bargain made is a bargain closed," replied Tyll merrily.

As soon as all his cakes were sold, Tyll went on his way again, and none could find him.

A Fool's Jest

Tyll wandered this way and that way until one day he came to the well-known city of Magdeburg. He stayed there a long time. Many of the people became his friends, for he was always supplying them with good laughter. In return for this pleasure they gave him plenty of food. Finally, the rich citizens, hearing of him and not wanting to be left out, asked him to come to the council. When they saw that he was only a young fellow, they told him they would not believe he was a jester unless he could prove it.

"So you don't believe, good fat citizens!" he thought to himself. "You would never even have noticed me if all the people had not spoken of me. Now you doubt their word. Do you believe in anything but your money-bags? Well, since you value them so much, you will have to pay me for giving you proof, and I will teach you a little lesson besides!"

He stood silent for a long time, thinking, and then he said, "I will show you a rare trick which you will remember for a long time. Only you must pay me, for it will be a valuable entertainment and will teach you a lesson as well. Masters, if you pay me twenty gold pieces," he continued, "I will fly without wings from the steeple of the town hall to the market-place. I want the money in advance, for you can see I risk breaking my neck."

Twenty gold pieces made a big sum, but the rich citizens figured that they would get it back quickly — if not from Tyll, then from someone else.

They paid him the money and fed him for three days as well, for he said he needed that much time to get ready.

The whole city had heard about the flight, and so, at the time set, the people were packed in the market-place like herrings. The officers came with their soldiers, who pushed many of the plain people back to make room for the rich. Soon Tyll was high up on the steeple, looking down on young and old, tall and short, their eyes wide open to see a man fly through the air.

Tyll looked at them a long time, shook his head solemnly, wiggled his ears, made a face like a monkey, and moved his arms a few times up and down. Then he waved his hands, danced a step or two, and began roaring with laughter.

He shouted down to them, "Noble citizens, I thought I was the only fool in your city, but now I see a city full of fools before me. If all of you together who run this place had told me that you would fly through the air without wings or feathers, I would not have believed you. Yet all of you wise men believed me, who am supposed to be only a clown. How could I fly, having no wings like a bird or a goose?"

He bade them a merry good day and was out of sight. The plain people, who were his friends, went home laughing, but the members of the council, who had given the money, were very angry. Yet they were ashamed to open their mouths, to show openly that a jester had made fools of them before all.

M. Jagendorf

GOOD SPORTS

CHILDREN OF THE SEA

THE fresh sea wind came sweeping over the land,
stirring the leaves of the birches in the churchyard.
Solvig, sitting on the stile between the churchyard and the
farm which was her home, was so unhappy that she neither
saw nor heard the old birch trees. She had been trying to
teach her pet gander, Gro-gos-a, or Gray Goose, how to
sing. Suddenly the pastor had come out of the church.

"What is the meaning of all this noise?" he wanted to know. "Don't you realize that we are having a wedding inside? It is not enough to shut up that gander of yours on Sundays. He disturbs every week-day service in the church also. If he honks once more I am going to tell your father to get rid of him. Is that understood?"

"Yes, Pastor."

"We are having a meeting this afternoon, and I expect him not to interrupt. You understand that also?"

"Yes, Pastor."

With one final glare at the gander, the pastor had marched back into the church.

"I can't see why Father bought a farm right next door to the church," Solvig thought. "Any other place in Norway would have been better."

With her chin in her hand, she sat there thinking. Gro-gos-a was an unusual gander. He was so wise that he knew far more than many people. As for his voice, it was not his fault that it was not beautiful. Solvig could not bear the thought of sending her pet to market and selling him for a few silver kroner.

She had not been sitting on the stile long when her brother Ola and the pastor's son Emmanuel came walking up the path.

"Come on with us to fish. We're going out for halibut. We want you to tend the lines while we row."

Solvig looked at the two boys for a moment. "I will go if I may take Gro-gos-a along."

"Why do you want to take a gander along?" asked the pastor's son.

Ola looked at Emmanuel coldly. The truth of the matter was that he, too, was fond of the gander. However, it would never do to let Emmanuel know that, and so he growled, "Let her take the gander along if she wants to."

The four of them set out for the fiord.

"We're going to strike out for the open sea," Emmanuel declared, as he pulled at the oars.

Solvig was surprised. "Did you ask your father if you might go out beyond the reefs?" she asked.

"No," said Emmanuel. "But the day is clear. There is no danger. Besides, the halibut bite best there."

Solvig knew that they were not supposed to go out so far, but she did not say anything more. She was sitting in the stern, still puzzling over what was to be done so that she would not have to give up her beloved gander. The boys pulled mightily at the oars, getting farther and farther from the shore.

Gro-gos-a stood in the bow and looked off across the sea. Now and then he honked sadly.

"What is the matter, Gro-gos-a?" asked Solvig once. "I am afraid you do not like boats."

Gro-gos-a did not become angry. He was used to

people who paid no attention to his words of wisdom. However, he did not stop honking.

"If that gander of yours is going to stand up there in the bow and honk the way he is doing, how do you think we are going to get any fish?" Emmanuel shouted. "Make him keep quiet, will you?"

"If you can shout, I guess it won't hurt if the gander says something now and then," Solvig declared. "If the fish are going to be scared at all, it is you who will scare them, not he."

"Oh, is that so, Miss Wise Tongue! Well, I can just tell you this, I am getting tired of listening to that gander of yours. He honks from morning until night."

"Yes, but Gro-gos-a does not bark in the middle of the night the way your dog does. I have never complained about that, even though I had to put up with him years before Gro-gos-a ever came to our place. So there!"

"Hey!" growled Ola. "How do you suppose we are going to get any fish if the two of you yell so loudly you can be heard for a mile?"

For a while they rowed on in silence, but it was not long before the gander gave a loud honk. Emmanuel took up an oar and was about to hit him, when Gro-gos-a jumped into the sea and set out for land.

"Now see what you have done!" Solvig cried. "You've scared the gander right out of the boat!"

"Good! Now we are rid of him and won't have to listen to his honking the rest of the afternoon!"

Solvig was upset. She was sure that the gander could not swim all the way back to shore. He was not a wild goose. "We must pull up the lines and go after him," she cried.

"We'll do nothing of the sort!" Emmanuel shouted. "This is my boat and I am not going to row you to shore."

"But you must," Solvig cried. "I am not going to have my gander drown!"

"Drown!" Emmanuel snorted. "Isn't that just like a girl! She thinks that a gander can drown!"

"Emmanuel," Solvig begged, "do turn the boat around and help me catch my gander." She was getting more and

more upset, for she knew that if the gander should reach the shore safely he would certainly go straight into the churchyard to crop grass. If he should honk just once more today, the pastor would surely tell her father about Gro-gos-a's sins, and her pet would have to be sold.

Once more she begged, a little angry now, "Turn back, Emmanuel, do you hear!"

"I came out to fish, and I don't mean to waste the rest of the day chasing after your old gander!"

"Emmanuel," Solvig threatened, "if you and Ola don't turn back right away, I am going to the pastor when I get ashore and tell him that you took us beyond the reefs today. You know he's warned you a dozen times that you must never row out this far from shore during the hurricane season."

"Oh, so you are a tattletale!"

No one in Norway wants to be known as a tattletale, but Solvig was willing to take even this shame upon herself, if only she could get Gro-gos-a back to safety again.

"We might as well turn back," Ola said, as though he were really in favor of continuing with the fishing, but wanted to stop the quarrel.

"All right, then," Emmanuel snapped. "But remember this, Solvig! It is the last time you go to sea with us!"

Emmanuel was so angry that his eyes flashed as he pulled at the oars. The gander was now merely a gray speck against the distant reefs. When they were within shouting distance, he climbed up on the first reef and sailed off.

Emmanuel dropped his oars. "Are you still afraid that your gander is going to drown?" he cried.

"Emmanuel! You take me right back to shore, or I will do just exactly as I said," Solvig ordered. Her cap sat straight upon her head now, like the comb on the head of a fighting cock.

The two boys took to rowing again. Suddenly, as they pulled at the oars, they heard a dull rumble behind them. All three looked back to sea. They knew that sound. It was a fearful one in the fiord country. Up from the horizon they saw a black cloud rising swiftly.

"A gale!" they cried.

In Norway such storms come up out of a clear sky. In half an hour's time they may whip the sea into high waves. Every time one strikes the fiord country it takes its harvest of lives among the fisher folk.

"Pull for your life!" Ola shouted.

64

Solvig said nothing. She just sat there watching the cloud that was bearing down upon them, and listening to the dull rumble grow into a thunder that seemed to shake both sea and sky.

They had passed the first row of reefs when they saw a white line along the rim of the horizon. It was spray flying before the storm. Then the sea struck them. It sent a shower of spray that soaked them to the skin.

They could not hear Gro-gos-a, standing on the shore, honking so loudly that the people came out of the church to see what was happening. Then the pastor and the others with him saw the black cloud and heard the rumble. Far out in the fiord they saw the three children in the boat.

They saw the wind strike them. A side wind!

"Oh! They'll never make it!" cried the pastor.

"Get into the big boat," somebody shouted. "We must row to meet them."

Solvig was bailing water out of the boat as fast as she could. The boat was filling rapidly and the sea threatened to upset them with every wave. The boys knew that they must get clear of the cliffs. The sea would pound them to bits if they were washed ashore there.

"Hold on to the side!" Ola shouted at Solvig.

Solvig did not have to be told what to do. She was a child of the sea. She clung to the side of the boat and bailed until her arm was stiff and her fingers were numb.

Then the sea lifted them high on the crest of a wave. The oars slipped out of the oarlocks, and the two boys were swept over the side into the sea.

Solvig forgot to bail. She clung to the side and waited. The boat leaped forward and dived into the next wave.

There was a terrific crash which seemed to shake all thoughts out of her head. Then everything became very still. She had been thrown forward and had knocked her head against the oarsman's seat, although she did not realize that until much later.

"Solvig, are you all right?"

Solvig looked up. Bending over her was her mother.

Slowly she realized that the boat had been flung ashore with her in it. Then she thought of the boys.

"Ola and Emmanuel!" she cried, trying to sit up. "Where are they?"

"They are safe," said her mother, pointing to the great eight-oared boat that was struggling toward the shore. The two boys were on board. The men had saved them.

Solvig sank back again. She was too weak in the knees to stand up. Something cold touched her upon the cheek. She looked and there was Gro-gos-a. She put her arm about the gander, for she realized now that had they not turned to follow the gander, they would never have made the shore alive.

That same evening after the storm was over, Ola and

66

Emmanuel came walking into the yard. Solvig was sitting upon the stile with her knitting, and Gro-gos-a was sitting on the step above her.

The two boys sat down beside Solvig. "It is about Gro-gos-a," they said. "We understand now that he saved our lives."

Solvig's needles flashed on.

"Father was very angry with me," Emmanuel continued, "for taking the boat out beyond the reefs. He said that Gro-gos-a was wiser than all of us put together. He said he would never say anything more about selling a gander that had saved three lives."

Solvig's eyes came up from her knitting and she smiled gratefully at the boys.

"Good night," they said, and walked off down the path.

"Good night," Solvig murmured happily.

Nora Burglon

DIGGING FOR TREASURE

I HAVE often thought that if the people who write books for children knew a little more, it would be better. I shall not tell you anything about us except what I should like to know if I was reading the story and you were writing it. I wonder that other authors have never thought of this.

We are the Bastables. There are six of us. Dora is the oldest. Then Oswald — and then Dicky. Oswald won the Latin prize at his school, and Dicky is good at sums. Alice and Noel are twins. They are ten, and Horace Octavius is my youngest brother. It is one of us that tells this story, but I shall not tell which. Only at the very end perhaps I will. While the story is going on, you may be trying to guess, only I bet you don't.

It was Oswald who first thought of looking for treasure. Oswald often thinks of very interesting things. And directly he thought of it he did not keep it to himself, as some boys would have done, but he told the others, and said, "I'll tell you what, we must go and dig for treasure."

"Yes, let's," said Dora.

Well, when we had agreed on this, we all went down into the cellar and lighted the gas. Oswald would have liked to dig there, but it is all flagstones. We looked among the old boxes and broken chairs and picture frames and empty bottles and things, and at last we found the spades we had for digging in the sand when we went to the sea-side three years ago. They are not silly, babyish, wooden spades, that split if you look at them, but good iron, with a blue mark across the top of the iron part, and yellow wooden handles. We wasted a little time getting them dusted, because the girls wouldn't dig with spades that had cobwebs on them.

First, we marked out a sort of square in the wild part of the garden, about three yards across, and began to dig. But we found nothing except worms and stones — and the ground was very hard.

So we thought we'd try another part of the garden, and we found a place in the big round flower bed, where the ground was much softer. We thought we'd make a smaller hole to begin with, and it was much better. We dug and dug and dug, and it was jolly hard work! We got very hot digging, but we found nothing.

Presently Albert-next-door looked over the wall. We do not like him very much, but we let him play with us sometimes. Albert is always very tidy. He wears fancy collars and velvet knickerbockers. I can't think how he can bear to.

So we said, "Hello!"

And he said, "What are you up to?"

"We're digging for treasure," said Alice. "Come over and help us. When we have dug deep enough we shall find a great pot of red clay, full of gold and precious jewels."

Albert-next-door only sniggered and said, "What silly nonsense!" He cannot play properly at all. It is very strange, because he has a very nice uncle. You see, Albert-next-door doesn't care for reading, and he has not read nearly so many books as we have, so he is very foolish and ignorant, but it cannot be helped, and you just have to put up with it when you want him to do anything.

So Oswald said, "Come and dig! Then you shall share the treasure when we've found it."

But he said, "I shan't. I don't like digging and I'm just going in to my tea."

"Come along and dig, there's a good boy," Alice said. "You can use my spade. It's much the best."

So he came along and dug, and when once he was over the wall we kept him at it, and we worked as well, of

course, and the hole got deep. Pincher worked, too. He is our dog and he is very good at digging. He digs for rats in the cellar, sometimes, and gets very dirty. But we love our dog, even when his face wants washing.

"I expect we shall have to make a tunnel," Oswald said, "to reach the rich treasure."

He jumped into the hole and began to dig at one side. After that we took it in turns to dig at the tunnel, and Pincher was most useful in scraping the earth out of the tunnel. He does it with his back feet when you say "Rats!" and he digs with his front ones, and burrows with his nose as well.

At last the tunnel was nearly a yard long, and big enough to creep along to find the treasure, if only it had been a bit longer. Now it was Albert's turn to go in and dig, but he refused.

"Take your turn like a man," said Oswald. Nobody can say that Oswald doesn't take his turn like a man. But Albert wouldn't. So we had to make him, because it was only fair.

"It's quite easy," Alice said, "you just crawl in and dig with your hands. Then when you come out, we can scrape out what you've done, with the spades. Come, be a man. You won't notice the dark in the tunnel if you shut your eyes tight. We've all been in except Dora, and she doesn't like worms."

"I don't like worms, either." Albert-next-door said this, but we remembered how he had picked a fat red-and-black worm up in his fingers, and thrown it at Dora only the day before.

So we put him in.

But he would not go in head first, the proper way, and

dig with his hands as we had done. Though Oswald was angry at the time, yet afterwards he owned that perhaps it was just as well. You should never be afraid to own that perhaps you were mistaken.

"Let me go in feet first," said Albert-next-door. "I'll dig with my boots. I will truly, honor bright."

So we let him go in feet first. He did it very slowly but at last he was in. Only his head stuck out into the hole.

"Now dig with your boots," said Oswald. "And, Alice, do catch hold of Pincher. He'll be digging again in another minute, and perhaps it would be uncomfortable for Albert if Pincher threw the dirt into his eyes."

You should always try to think of these little things. Thinking of other people's comfort makes them like you. Alice held Pincher, and we all shouted, "Kick! Dig with your feet, for all you're worth!"

So Albert-next-door began to dig with his feet, and we stood on the ground over him, waiting — and all in a minute the ground gave way, and we tumbled together in a heap. When we got up, there was a little shallow hollow where we had been standing, and Albert-next-door was underneath, stuck quite fast, because the roof of the tunnel had tumbled in on him. He is a horribly unlucky boy.

It was dreadful the way he cried and screamed, though he had to own it didn't hurt, only it was rather heavy and he couldn't move his legs. While we were trying to dig

73

him out, Dicky climbed over the wall, to tell the cook there to tell Albert-next-door's uncle he had been buried by mistake, and to come and help dig him out.

Dicky was a long time gone. We wondered what had become of him. All the while, the screaming went on and on, for we had taken the loose earth off Albert's face so that he could scream quite easily and comfortably.

Presently Dicky came back and Albert-next-door's uncle came with him. He has very long legs and his hair is light and his face is brown. He has been to sea, but now he writes books. I like him.

He told his nephew to stow it, so Albert did. Then he asked him if he was hurt, and Albert had to say he wasn't, for though he is a coward and very unlucky, he is not a liar like some boys.

'This promises to be a long, if agreeable, task," said Albert-next-door's uncle, rubbing his hands and looking at the hole with Albert's head in it. "I will get another spade." So he fetched the big spade out of the next-door garden tool-shed and began to dig his nephew out.

"Mind you keep very still," he said, "or I might chunk a bit out of you with the spade."

After a while he said, "My curiosity is excited. I own that I should like to know how my nephew happened to be buried. But don't tell me if you'd rather not. I suppose no force was used?"

"Only moral force," said Alice. They used to talk a lot about moral force at the school where she went. In case you don't know what it means, I'll tell you that it is making people do what they don't want to, just by laughing at them or promising them things if they're good.

"Only moral force, hmm?" said Albert-next-door's uncle. "Well?"

"Well," Dora said, "I'm very sorry it happened to Albert. I'd rather it had been one of us. It would have been my turn to go into the tunnel, only I don't like worms, so they let me off. You see we were digging for treasure."

"Yes," said Alice, "and I think we were just coming to the underground passage that leads to the treasure, when the tunnel fell in on Albert. He is so unlucky," and she sighed.

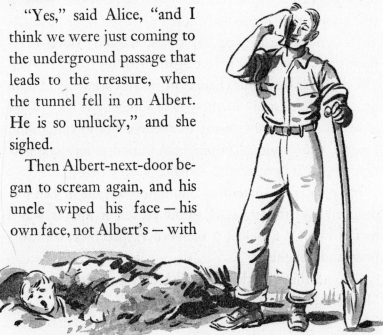

Then Albert-next-door began to scream again, and his uncle wiped his face — his own face, not Albert's — with his silk handkerchief, and then he put it in his trousers pocket. It seems a strange place to put a handkerchief, but he had his coat and waistcoat off, and I suppose he wanted the handkerchief handy. Digging is warm work.

He told Albert-next-door to drop it, or he wouldn't rescue him, so Albert stopped screaming, and presently his uncle finished digging him out. Albert did look so funny, with his hair all dusty and his face muddy with earth and crying.

We all said how sorry we were, but he wouldn't say a word back to us. He was sick to think he'd been the one buried, when it might just as well have been one of us. I felt myself that it was hard lines.

"So you were digging for treasure," said Albert-next-door's uncle, wiping his face again with his handkerchief. "Well, I fear that your chances of success are small. I have made a careful study of the whole subject. What I don't know about buried treasure is not worth knowing. And I never knew more than one coin buried in any one garden, and that is generally — hello, what's that?"

He pointed to something shining in the hole he had just dragged Albert out of. Oswald picked it up. It was a half crown. We looked at each other, speechless with surprise and delight.

"Well, that's lucky," said Albert-next-door's uncle. "Let's see, that's fivepence each for you."

"It's fourpence and something. I can't do fractions," said Dicky. "There are seven of us, you see."

"Oh, do you count Albert as one of yourselves?"

"Of course," said Alice, "and, I say, he was buried after all. Why shouldn't we let him have the odd somethings, and we'll have fourpence each."

We all agreed to this, and told Albert-next-door we would bring his share as soon as we could get the half crown changed. He cheered up a little at that, and his uncle wiped his face again — he did look hot — and began to put on his coat and waistcoat.

When he had done it, he stooped and picked up something. He held it up, and you will hardly believe it, but it is quite true — it was another half crown!

"To think that there should be two!" he said. "In all my experience of buried treasure I never heard of such a thing!"

I wish Albert-next-door's uncle would come treasure-seeking with us regularly. He must have very sharp eyes, for Dora says she was looking just the minute before at the very place where the second half crown was picked up and she never saw it.

P.S. It is Oswald that has been telling this story, in case you haven't guessed.

E. Nesbit

RED BLIZZARD

ALL day it had been dark, but when Guy Turner came out of school and saw the sky, he was frightened. He had come from Ohio only the year before, to live with his uncle on a cattle station in Queensland, but between going to school in Melbourne and spending holidays on the cattle station, he already felt like an Australian. While in Melbourne, he lived with his sister and her husband, Terry Sloan. He knew, from the many tales they told, how everyone dreaded dust storms.

The sun was in a pink fog, and in the northwest were thick dark clouds that looked like red thunder-heads. It

was not the coming dust storm that frightened him, however. He was afraid Doctor Newman's expedition would
set out without him. With the big dust storms of the
season starting, the Doctor would be leaving soon to study
the wind erosion in the big Mallee Land wheat belt.

Mallee is a kind of eucalyptus bush. It grows low and
thick, like a hedge, with five or six trunks from one root,
and none bigger around than your arm. It is so stiff the
wind cannot bend it. Twenty-five thousand square miles
in the State of Victoria used to be covered with mallee.
Then a settler who had cleared some land found the red
soil was rich, and planted wheat. Other settlers followed
his example.

Before men cleared and plowed the land in this dry
region, there were some dust storms, but they were not
bad, because the roots of mallee grew close together
and held the soil, so that little
of it was blown away. When
people began to clear the land
of mallee bushes, there was
nothing to hold the soil and
the dust storms became red
blizzards. Even some of the
sheep lands had been spoiled
by dust. Australia cannot
allow this to go on, for it is

the biggest wool-producing country in the world. That's why Doctor Newman was making an expedition into Mallee Land.

Guy had not been asked to go with Doctor Newman, but still he had not asked if he might go and been turned down, either. So he tore down the Sydney Road in Melbourne and crossed Gratten Street to reach the University.

He went up the steps of the University three at a time, and rushed down the empty halls to Doctor Newman's room. When he finally reached the door, there were five or six men in the room, all staring at him.

"Where's the fire, Guy?" Doctor Newman asked. "We thought the whole department was coming."

"I'm sorry," Guy said and slid over to a seat behind Terry Sloan. "I was afraid you might have gone without me."

A man named Mr. Bender grinned. "What do you mean, 'without you'?"

Guy's face turned red. "I mean without my having a chance to ask if I could go to the Mallee Land with you. I could do all the work about the horses, see to their meals, and water them, pack the loads, and everything."

"Sorry, Guy," Doctor Newman said. "I'm afraid this isn't your lucky day. We aren't even taking horses. We're going by car and there wouldn't be room for you."

80

This sounded final, but Guy had one more plan in mind. He did not say anything about it. He said he would be there to help them load the car next morning.

On the way home, Guy bought some bread, a pound of butter, two cans of sardines, and a glass of peanut butter. The next morning he got up in the dark. Then he made six sets of sandwiches — enough for lunch and supper that day, for breakfast, lunch, and supper the next day, and for breakfast the third day. He wrapped up enough tea and sugar for six meals and filled his canteen with water. Terry had already packed part of the back of the car for an early start. Guy now unrolled Terry's blankets and put his own blankets and his mosquito net in with them. Terry might think the roll looked fat, but he would not guess the reason — at least, Guy hoped not.

When Doctor Newman and the other members of the party arrived, Guy looked empty-handed and helpful. They packed their things, then began watching for the fifth man, who belonged to the Department of Agriculture. At last the Doctor telephoned to know what was delaying him.

"Too bad," he reported, when he came away from the phone. "George's father and mother were hurt in an accident last night, and George is tied up at the hospital. We'll have to go without him."

Guy's eyes gleamed with excitement.

Doctor Newman looked over and said kindly, "We might have had room for you after all, Guy, if you had had your blankets ready. We can't wait now."

He took the front seat beside Terry, who was driving. Mr. Bender and Mr. Parker, the fourth man, got into the back seat. Guy climbed in, too.

"That's all right," he tried to say calmly. "I put my emergency kit in the car, just in case of — well, an emergency."

Mr. Bender gave a suspicious grin, and Terry raised his eyebrows. The Doctor turned around and saw Guy squeezed into the seat. "Oh, let him come," he said.

The rest of the day was like riding on pink clouds for Guy. The roads off the main highways were rough, and the heat terrific, but Guy was feeling so pleased that he did not mind a few hardships.

Mildura, the largest town in the wheat belt, for which they were aiming, was nearly three hundred miles from Melbourne. They had started so early, however, that they were in the Mallee Land by late afternoon.

"Awful-looking stuff," Mr. Bender shouted at Doctor Newman over the noise of the car. They were going through a stretch of land that had never been cleared of mallee bushes.

Meantime, the dust was growing worse with every mile. Finally, the road became so drifted in dust that Terry

82

could hardly push the car through. They went more and more slowly, running in low gear and having to put water in the radiator time after time.

"We'll never get to Mildura tonight," Mr. Bender said. Everybody agreed with him.

"We're coming to a side road. Let's see what the sign says." The sign pointed west — "Kangaburra Station — 24 miles."

This was one of the farms they were supposed to visit. The road was simply two deep ruts, thick with dust.

"Think it's safe to try it?" Terry asked. "We might stick in the sand."

"We can walk if we have to," said Mr. Bender.

They turned off and struggled along this track until they began to go through mallee scrub again. Some places had been burned by brush fires and were lonely looking deserts with nothing alive on them but flies, hawks, and crows. The dust storm now blew more densely, and dust rose up behind the car like the wake from an ocean liner. Nobody said anything for a long time.

Terry had to stop the car during blasts of dust. He couldn't see. He began to doubt whether he was on the road.

"I can see ruts," Doctor Newman reported, peering through the car window. "They look far less deep than before, though."

"Maybe that is because they're filled with dust."

"Why didn't we come prepared to camp and to eat?" Terry groaned. They had brought blankets and mosquito nets but no food. Of course they had water. Nobody travels without it in Australia.

After the next dust spell the car would not start. "I think the motor is choked with dust," Terry said. He got out to look at the country round about them.

In a little while he began shouting. The others answered, and he steered by the sound of their voices. When he appeared he said, "I've found something. It's bad news, too. This track we've been following ends up a little way beyond at an old empty shack."

"A shack? That's not bad news," the Doctor said.

They left the car in the road and stumbled after Terry with their blankets and water. The wind, once they were out of the car, was a red blizzard. They were all choked and coughing from the dust before they could get inside the shack and slam the door.

"Now aren't you sorry you came?" Doctor Newman asked Guy.

"Oh, this isn't bad," he shouted back. He had to yell to be heard above the noise of the wind.

There was a mud fireplace in the shack, and the dead mallee trunks made good wood to burn in it. Terry built a little fire for cheerfulness. When it was blazing, the Doctor began undoing the straps of his blanket roll. There was just floor space enough for everyone to spread out his blankets.

The dust was streaming into the room through cracks in the walls, and the one little window rattled, sounding as if it might give way any minute. Terry turned away from the fire when the blaze started, and came over between the Doctor and Guy, who was sitting on the floor

85

with his emergency roll between his feet. Mr. Bender and Mr. Parker sat on a bench against the far wall. Even the far wall was only ten feet from the fire.

"We were foolish not to bring food," Terry said.

"We expected to hit plenty of big stations before night. Who would think we would end up here, lost in the mallee! Fellows used to get lost here and go mad. They would throw their clothes away and die of thirst. But who would think of its happening to us!"

"I'm not going to throw my clothes away," Mr. Bender said.

"You're going to starve to death," said Terry.

Guy felt like laughing, but got out his mouth organ instead.

"Music," scoffed Terry, "when we need food!"

Guy did not answer, but played "Home, Sweet Home" and "I'll be down to get you in a taxi, Honey."

By and by Terry said hungrily, "We could have carried a little package of tea as easily as not."

"You're right," Mr. Parker agreed. He turned to Guy. "You seem pretty cheerful."

"Of course," Guy said. Then he added carelessly, "This music is just to make sure I have a good appetite."

"Oh, yes? Now you're being funny."

"I'm not fooling. I'll be eating pretty soon."

"The boy's crazy."

86

But Terry was staring at the luggage. "Listen, Guy. Are those things blankets in your emergency kit?"

"No, I rolled mine up with yours."

Then, as nobody spoke, he decided it was time for the big surprise. He untied his roll while they watched, and finally came to the six packages, one for each of six meals.

Guy arranged them in a circle, and put two small packages in the middle. "These are the tea and the sugar," he explained. "But we haven't anything to boil water in."

They stared at the packages, then at one another. Their expressions were more fun than anything they could have said. Finally, Mr. Bender asked in a solemn voice, "How much tea is there?"

Guy told him there was enough for six meals for one person. He added, "I'll find something to boil it in or bust."

It was Doctor Newman who found an old kettle with a hole in it. They scrubbed it with sand and stuffed the hole with a piece of clean handkerchief. Then Terry sacrificed a little water to boil in the bottom so that any germs that might be in the kettle would be killed. They finally made tea, and shared it, taking turns with the cup Guy had brought.

"Which package of sandwiches do you want, sir?" Guy asked Doctor Newman. "They're all peanut butter or sardines, my favorites."

87

"My favorites, too," Mr. Bender sighed, with smiles.

Terry stooped down and read the labels on the packages: "Tuesday noon, Tuesday supper, Wednesday breakfast —" Then he looked at the Doctor and laughed. The Doctor pretended his choice was important.

"I'll take Tuesday supper."

After a long time of eating, Mr. Parker said, "I didn't know sardines could taste so good."

"Or peanut butter," said Terry.

After the tea and sandwiches, the blanket beds were made ready for the night. Guy thought he had never had such fun camping anywhere as by the fire in the little shack. He did not even mind the dust.

Next day they found that they were not far from a big station, after all. The Doctor's party stayed there two days, studying the effect of the red blizzard, and then went on to the region where wonderful drought-resistant crops — certain varieties of wheat and corn — had been planted.

When they stopped for lunch on the way back, the Doctor said, "Shall we take a vote to see who has shown up best on this trip?"

"We don't need to," said Mr. Bender, and they all looked at Guy.

Margaret I. Ross

THE LORDLY KITE

FINDERS, KEEPERS

SLOWLY Hassan opened his eyes and stretched his aching knees. Oh, but it was cold! It must be very early. The sun was not up yet, though the sky was growing light. Not even the turbaned men who cleaned out the gutters of Adana were about.

"There's no sense in lying still and freezing to death," Hassan thought. Stiffly he crawled out of the covering in which he had wrapped himself for the night. The chill of the stones under his bare feet set him dancing up and down, while he settled his cap over his dark hair, shook out his baggy black trousers, drew in his girdle, and pulled his ragged coat closer about him.

Now there was the business of getting some breakfast. He was hungry as a wolf after his long sleep in the open.

"First, I'll go to the public fountain and wash the sleep from my eyes and get a good drink of fresh water," he decided. "Then I'll go and start cleaning out Ali's stables. When he comes and finds the work half done, he'll be pleased and give me enough to buy hot tea and a roll."

He went down the street and turned round the corner toward the great square.

He stopped suddenly. He had almost stepped on the most beautiful kite he had ever seen in his life. It was a kite fit for a prince, striped in glowing red and blue, with a fine long tail and a bunch of string that surely would be long enough to fly the kite high over the housetops.

Yet here it lay on the muddy cobblestones of the street. Probably it had blown off some roof during the night. Emin, the son of the rich leather merchant, lived in the great house right above the spot where the kite lay. Yes, it must be Emin's kite.

"I could take this kite," Hassan told himself excitedly, "and no one would know. If it is Emin's, his father is rich enough to buy him material to make a hundred more."

Every spring, for as long as he could remember, Hassan had wanted a kite. A thousand times he had watched luckier boys flying theirs from the roofs of the town on bright windy days, and sometimes he felt that he could not bear it if he could not have one too.

Far down the street a shutter banged open. A voice cried, "Away with you!" to some dog. The town was waking up.

90

Without another second's thought, Hassan swooped down on his find. Carefully he gathered the beautiful tail and the bundle of string into his arms. Hiding the kite as well as he could under his loose garment, he ran like the wind down the alleys toward Ali's stables.

Here was something to puzzle about, he thought as he ran. He could not remember having ever before owned a single thing that he could not carry easily about his person. He wore all his clothes all the time. He tucked away in his wide girdle such things as a knife he had found, a coin now and then, or some dried figs that he was saving for tomorrow's meal. But a kite must be kept from the weather, and from the sight of envious eyes.

Far back in the storerooms where Ali kept his hay, Hassan knew of a corner, dark, but dry and safe, which was just the place for a kite.

All that morning Hassan worked hard for Ali. First, he cleaned out the horses' stalls. Then he stood at the horses' heads while Ali curried them. Then, without being told, he started putting fresh hay in the mangers.

"What has come over the boy?" Ali exclaimed at last. "Never before has Hassan worked for more than five minutes at a time. If you expect poor old Ali to pay you for all this, you had better be off with you."

"It is not the pay I want," Hassan explained earnestly. "This morning when I woke and saw the snow beginning to go from the mountains, I thought, 'Spring is coming. Soon I will be eleven years old. I will be a man in a few years. I might want to have a house then, and bring a pretty wife to live in it. I'll have to have a trade. And if I learn how to care for horses, then perhaps I can have a stable, and earn a good living for all my children.' "

"Fine talk!" said Ali gruffly. "And how long will these good intentions last? Tell me that!"

But he did not drive Hassan away. He even gave him bread and cheese for breakfast. Later he showed him how to saddle Lightning, the fine horse the Turkish captain would ride that day.

At noon Ali went upstairs for his lunch. "I will watch the horses for you while you are gone," Hassan promised him.

"You'll watch, no doubt, until your friend Mehmet comes along and says, 'How about a game of marbles?' After that my stables will be left to look after themselves. I know! I'll lock up today just as I always do." Ali barred the door and went his way.

Hassan grinned, and jumped so high into the air that his heels came together twice before he reached the earth again. "So much the better for me," he told himself. "My kite is safe enough here by itself for a while. I'll go to the bazaar and see what's going on."

Mehmet's grandfather kept a bakery at the edge of the

bazaar. Near the door at the back, Hassan stopped and gave two short barks like a street dog. For years this had been the signal between him and his friend.

Mehmet opened the door a little. "I can't come out now, Hassan," he said. "I have to watch the loaves that are baking in the oven. What's new?"

"Have you been in the bazaar this morning?"

"Yes, all morning I was out delivering cakes."

"Has anyone lost a fine red and blue kite?"

"Emin was making a big noise about a kite he said someone stole from his roof last night."

Hassan jumped up and down with excitement. "I thought so!" He came close to Mehmet and whispered in his ear, "I found Emin's kite in the street below his father's house. Promise you won't tell a soul?"

"Of course I won't tell!"

"If it were your kite, Mehmet, I would give it back. But Emin can buy a hundred more. So finders, keepers."

"Is the kite any good?"

"Oh, Mehmet, you should see it! It's bigger than any kite that's ever been flown over the square, and it's got a tail — so long — with three colors worked into it."

"But if Emin should see you flying it!" Mehmet was as excited as Hassan now.

"I know!" Hassan wrinkled his brow. "There will be trouble then."

"What's more," Mehmet went on, "there's no use your talking of flying your kite from the roofs. You haven't got a roof. None of our friends have really good roofs. My grandfather's roof is no good to us — it's the lowest in the town."

"I know all that," Hassan said stoutly. "But never mind. I will surely think of a way. Did I not manage a shelter for my kite? I will take care of Emin, too, and I will get a roof. You'll see!"

"You think you're the sultan himself!" laughed Mehmet.

"Mehmet, Mehmet, you good-for-nothing!" A woman's angry voice called from inside the shop.

"The bread! I forgot all about it!" Mehmet rushed inside the door.

Hassan barked twice again, by way of farewell, and turned away toward Ali's stables.

Fair Exchange

Half of the boys of Adana were watching a company of soldiers drilling on the dusty parade ground. Hassan saw Emin at the edge of the crowd, and moved close to him. "I'll be able to think of a way sooner if I know Emin's mind," he told himself.

When the soldiers had marched away, Emin, Hassan, and a dozen other boys stayed on, some to play mumble-ty-peg and some, marbles.

Suddenly, above the chatter of the games, Hassan heard Emin's voice raised importantly. "My father is going to Aintab next week. He rides at the head of a train of twenty mules."

"Will you go with him, Emin?" asked Ahmed.

"No," Emin sighed. "There is no horse for me to ride."

Then it was that Hassan thought of a way. So magnificent was the idea that he had to clap his hand over his mouth to keep from shouting.

"What has struck you, Hassan?" Omar asked impatiently, waiting for Hassan to shoot his marble.

"Never you mind!" Hassan returned. "I have business."

Later that morning Hassan stood holding Yildiz for Ali to groom.

"This is the pony you are anxious to sell, is it not, Master?" Hassan asked Ali.

"Yes, yes. I would like well enough to sell him, but wishes are one thing, and money in the pocket is another. Who, I would like to know, wants a horse this size?"

"Emin's father, the leather merchant, is going on a journey," Hassan said. His bright eyes watched Ali's expression. "He would like to take Emin, but he has no horse for him to ride. Yildiz might be just the right horse for a boy Emin's age."

"For Emin, the leather merchant's son?" Ali's eyes narrowed with interest. "Emin's father can pay well. There might be something to this. We shall see."

Hassan ran off to find Mehmet. Emin would soon have the horse he wanted. Emin would go off on a journey and he, Hassan, could fly the lordly kite over the roofs of Adana.

Mehmet's black eyes sparkled when he heard the plan. "You always do think of something, Hassan. Allah made you a clever one. If only it all works out!"

Hassan and Mehmet were part of the watching crowd a week later when Emin's father was ready to start for Aintab.

"A fine day for a journey it is!" Hassan heard the fruit seller say to Emin's father. "You are lucky to have a son riding with you. May your journey be fortunate!"

96

Proudly the leather merchant received the good wishes
of his friends and acquaintances, while Emin put Yildiz
through his paces.

"Want to see him gallop?" he shouted to the admiring
crowd. Away he went, half-way around the square.

There he wheeled and came slowly back toward the bazaar again, reining in tightly to make Yildiz arch his neck and dance.

"Emin is pleased," Hassan thought to himself. "He is far more pleased with the pony I managed to get for him than he was with the kite I kept from him. So everything is all right, and the kite is mine — " He stopped, his face clouded with sudden doubt.

Was what he had just said to himself true? Was everything all right? Was the kite really his? The more he thought, the more that uncomfortable little doubt stayed in his mind. He had been so busy, and so excited since the morning when he found the kite, that he had not stopped to consider the matter clearly.

But now he saw! There was no getting away from it. He had kept Emin's kite, knowing it was Emin's. He was little better than a thief. The kite was not really his at all.

He saw Emin slowly walking Yildiz up and down at the end of the square. For the moment no one was near him. Hassan knew what he must do.

He dashed across to Yildiz's side, caught hold of the bridle, and looked up at Emin. "Emin, you know your red and blue kite? It blew into the street one night. I — I know where it is. Do you want it back, Emin?"

Hassan swallowed hard. It had been difficult to say all that to Emin.

Emin was surprised at Hassan's news. "My red and blue kite? So that's where it went. But I got a new kite after I lost that one. And what do I want with kites, now that I am journeying with my father? Let the kite be yours, Hassan, if it is any good to you."

Hassan drew a deep breath that was half a sob of relief.

The rich merchant's procession was moving now, and Emin galloped off to take his place by his father's side. Mule-drivers were shouting to their animals. The crowd from the bazaar was shouting good wishes. "Allah be with you! Farewell!"

Hassan, his eyes shining, his heart pounding, leaped in the air, clicked his heels together, and shouted louder than all the rest, "Allah be with you, Emin!"

The dust kicked up by the mules and horses blew into his eyes, until he could no longer see the pack train.

"Oh, what a wind!" growled the fruit seller.

Hassan seized Mehmet by the shoulder. "What a wind for sailing our kite here over the square!" he shouted. "Come on, Mehmet! Come on!"

Marie Abbott and *Dorothea Blaisdell*

CLIMB BY MOONLIGHT

The Accident

"Merry, it's full moon tonight!" said Uncle Tony.

"Yes, I know it is," said his niece, Meredith, eagerly waiting to hear what would follow.

"But don't you see what it means? We can climb up the slope of the Gifferhorn by day, go as far as we like, build a fire, cook our supper, then wait for darkness — and the moon will light our way home!"

"Oh, Uncle Tony, what a wonderful idea!" Merry cried. "But Michael won't be back in time to go with us."

Uncle Tony was silent for a moment. "We can't waste a full moon, Merry," he urged, "when we have only six weeks in Switzerland. Perhaps we could do it again with your brother. Besides, he's going to have a fine day with his school friends."

Merry smiled. Moonlight in the Alps!

"Frau Egli could give Michael his supper," she planned happily. "She'd be glad to, because Fritz is away guiding some people up the Matterhorn."

In the afternoon Merry gathered a pack and Uncle Tony left a note for Michael, saying:

Merry and I took our supper to the Gifferhorn.
Frau Egli has yours waiting for you at her chalet.
We're coming home by moonlight. Don't wait up.
UNCLE TONY

Uncle Tony shouldered the pack. "My, but it's heavy for a hot day! What is in it, Merry?"

"Oh," she looked at him and laughed, "just the food, a blanket, and one or two books."

"Merry!" he said, trying to sound very stern. "Can't you go anywhere without one or two books? When are we going to have time to read them?"

"There might be lots of time before the moon rises high enough to light our way down into the valley."

"And I suppose we'll read by the light of the fire until then! All right. But, Merry, we've got to take jackets and things."

"Jackets in this heat?"

"The temperature changes quickly in the mountains and tonight may be very cold."

It was five o'clock when they left. The heavy August heat lay over the valley, and the sun was glaring on the white dust of the road.

They took a path that wound up the side of the mountain through dry pastures. They walked slowly on, single file, up the narrow trail that grew steeper with every mile. Once they passed a peasant with a load of hay on a light wooden sleigh. Smooth runners, high and rounded in front, held the hay in place.

"What a strange way to move hay!" Merry exclaimed, remembering the hay carts with their strong horses at home in England.

"He's taking it down to his barn from some high hut

where it's been stored," Uncle Tony explained. "A load of hay can easily be moved down the grassy slopes in this sleigh."

Merry looked around just in time to see the peasant steering the sleigh into a shed which they had passed on the path. Then they went by a spring, where they stopped to fill their rubber bucket with fresh water. Soon, now, the air began to cool.

The path had begun to cross the slope sideways and walking was easier. They came to a wide ledge where scrubby trees grew among the rocks. Grass grew in patches, and the ground was dotted with bits of wood from trees blown over long ago and dried by the sun.

"A good place for a camp," Uncle Tony said, glancing around him and lowering his pack.

The sun had slipped behind the rock wall in the distance, its rays pointing upward. Uncle Tony and Merry were still in clear daylight on the heights. Below them in the valley was the gloom of approaching night.

"It's lovely just to watch the light go from the west in yellow and flood the east in pink!"

"It is," agreed Uncle Tony, "but darkness won't be long in falling on us. See, down in the valley, lights are coming on in the chalets. We've got to make camp, Merry, before the light goes. It will be a long time before the moon is bright enough to show us anything."

103

Uncle Tony began to build a fireplace, moving flat stones into position. Merry gathered sticks for their fire and unpacked the blanket and the food from the pack.

Soon the fire was crackling gaily. Merry put the frying pan on and began to cook the bacon. Uncle Tony cleared a place in the coals for their coffee pot to rest. When the bacon was fried, Merry took it from the pan and laid it between thick slices of buttered bread. Then she dropped eggs into the hot fat, their whites curling up and the yolks turning firm. She placed one each on the bacon, and, closing the sandwiches, passed Uncle Tony's to him.

"A mountaineer's meal," he grinned, as he poured out the bubbling coffee.

They ate in silence, one or the other tossing wood on the fire from time to time. Then Merry opened a package of ginger cake and cut big pieces of it.

"Shall we have our oranges now or save them for later?"

"Let's have them now."

They cut holes in the tops and sucked them slowly while the fire died down and night came over the world.

In the valley below, a train was moving, leaving a fiery tail. "Michael will be home soon," said Merry softly.

Then a thread of silver, marking the line of the river, appeared down in the valley. A rooftop gleamed here and there, and the white spire of the tiny church stood out plainly. The moon, rising behind the mountain on which they had made their camp, would fill the valley with light before it rose high enough to touch the western slope of the Gifferhorn.

Uncle Tony stirred. "We can't leave yet for a half hour or so and we'll need the fire. I'm going to get more wood." He rose slowly, stiff from lying on the ground.

"Shall I help you?" asked Merry.

"No, thanks."

There was a rim of light by the fire, but beyond it all was dark. Uncle Tony stumbled off, humming to himself, and was lost in the blackness. Merry curled up by the fire and closed her eyes.

Suddenly there was a loud crash. Uncle Tony, his arms full of wood, had tripped in the dark and lay on the ground within a few feet of the fire. At first he did not move and then he raised his head and smiled — a thin smile.

Merry dropped down beside him. "Oh, Uncle Tony, I'm so sorry. Are you hurt? Take my arm and I'll help you."

He shook his head, pulling at his legs. "It's all right,

really, only my feet must be caught by a rock I loosened. I don't seem to be able to move them."

Merry threw some of the wood on the fire so that its light might show her what to do. Then her quick fingers felt along the earth and rock where Uncle Tony's feet were caught, to see if she could free them.

"Does it hurt, Uncle Tony?" she asked.

He shook his head. "No, it doesn't. I don't think the whole weight is on my feet."

He shifted his position and found that one leg stirred. Reaching down with his hands, he pulled on it with all his might, but the rock held fast.

The moon came over the Gifferhorn ridge and Merry, seeing more clearly the size of the rock, knew it was hopeless to think of moving it. There was only one thing to do — get help at once.

"Uncle Tony," she said, trying to sound calm. "I'm going down to the village for help. We can't move the rock by ourselves."

"Wait, Merry, there must be something we can do. We might signal with the fire or our voices," he suggested.

"It's no good, Uncle Tony," she said. "The lights have gone out all over the valley. I've been watching them."

She put her hand in his. Then she got up quickly, working while she talked. "I'll build up the fire and leave some wood near for you to throw on, and you can read my books. You'll probably be glad I brought them!"

She moved the bucket of water near in case he became thirsty, spread the blanket over him, pulled off her leather jacket, and folded it into a pillow.

"Why don't you wait for the moon to light your path, Merry? It won't be long now."

Merry looked toward the valley. "I'll be all right," she said bravely. Although the first streaks of light were indeed finding their way onto the Gifferhorn's slope, the descent itself still lay locked in darkness.

"Don't get all the village out whatever you do."

"No, I won't." Merry knew how he would hate that. "I'll get Fritz, and we'll be back before you know it."

Uncle Tony nodded. In his heart he knew it would be three hours at least.

She knelt down and kissed him lightly. "Comfortable?"

He smiled. "Very!"

She was gone. He heard her walking lightly, carefully, down the steep slope. Then he could hear her footsteps no longer. He pulled once more at his legs and groaned when they would not move.

Reaching toward the fire where her books sat one upon the other, he drew the first to him and opened it.

"*The Technique of Mountain Climbing*," he read slowly, smiling.

THE RESCUE

Merry ran, whenever she could see far enough ahead of her down the path. Twice she tripped over stones, and once she nearly missed a turning, for most of the slope still lay in darkness, with only occasional patches of light.

When the path lay white before her she ran swiftly, careful not to disturb stones. When the path dipped through pines and only a glimmer of light lay on it, she went more slowly. Nothing would be gained if she lost her way.

Two thoughts drew her on: one of Uncle Tony on the Gifferhorn's ledge, and the other of Fritz, so skilled from years of guiding. Fritz would move the rock and set Uncle Tony free.

When she reached the road and the full moonlight, she ran more swiftly. She crossed the little bridge over the Turbach and sped up the valley. She hurried past their chalet, where Michael must be sleeping peacefully. Rounding the bend in the road, she reached the Eglis' chalet.

She raised her hand to knock — then let it drop like a weight to her side. The smile fled from her face. She had entirely forgotten that Fritz was away with some climbers

108

on the Matterhorn! Merry could not move. To waken Frau Egli would do no good and would upset her. Yet if Merry went down to the village, whom could she call upon for help? Rossli, the baker? Old Knubel, the postman? Wake one, and they would all come.

"Don't get all the village out," Uncle Tony had said.

"No, Uncle Tony, I won't," she had answered.

What should she do? Michael — !

Merry flew back down the road to their chalet. "Michael," she said, standing over him and putting her hand lightly on his shoulder. He opened his eyes and smiled sleepily.

"Have a — nice — time?" he muttered, and his eyes closed again.

"Michael!"

His eyes opened. He looked at her. Something in her white face made him sit up, wide awake.

"Merry, what's the matter?"

"Listen, Michael, Uncle Tony's on the Gifferhorn. A big rock fell over and pinned his legs down — "

Michael was out of bed. "Let's get Fritz to go back with us."

"Fritz is away."

"Well, I'm here. I'll be ready in a minute. Hurry, Merry, get Uncle Tony's rope."

Merry dashed from the room. Rope and extra sweaters

were bundled into a pack, while she heated some milk to fill a thermos bottle to take with them.

They closed the door behind them and started up the road, walking quickly. Their high mountain world was bathed in the cold, bright August moonlight.

"Oh, Michael, do you think you can lift the rock?" Merry asked. It was a comfort to have someone to share her worry.

"Of course, but if I can't, we can do it between us. That's why I said to bring the rope."

They walked along in silence. Neither one wore nailed boots, but rubber-soled shoes, so that their footsteps fell lightly.

"Do you think his feet are hurt, crushed or anything, Merry?"

"No, I don't," she said. "There was a hollow in the earth where he fell, and some twisted roots held his feet."

"You don't think the rock is really touching them?"

She shook her head and looked up the mountain ahead of them. "Oh," she cried, "the Gifferhorn is in light now! That must be comforting to him up there all alone."

"Wasn't the moon on it when you came down?"

"No, just here and there. It was mostly in darkness until I got down through the pine woods."

Michael whistled. "How did you find your way?"

"I — I don't know, Michael. It just seemed to be there."

"I don't expect he'll be able to walk, Merry."

"Oh, but why not, if his feet aren't hurt?"

"Because they'll be so numb from being pinned like that. If only we could make a stretcher! But we have nothing to make it of."

The path was steeper now. They passed a hay hut, the last shelter before they reached the ledge. A faint smell of hay came from the hut as they went by and Merry recalled the peasant they had met and his sleigh. His sleigh!

"Michael!" Merry stopped and grasped his arm. "We passed a peasant when we were coming up, and he was steering a sleigh into this very shed!"

Michael's eyes shone in the moonlight. "Just the thing, Merry."

"But, Michael, it isn't ours."

Michael thought for a moment. "We're only borrowing it, Merry. Fritz says that on the mountains it's all right to do anything in an emergency."

They approached the hay hut. Michael pulled at the door. It was not locked, and as it came open a wave of warm, sweet air struck their faces. There stood the sleigh.

They steered it out of the hut and shut the door carefully behind them. Each grasped one of the rounded runners, and moved up the path, the sleigh light as an empty shell between them.

Uncle Tony heard them coming from a distance — light steps hurrying up the side of the mountain and hushed voices in the night. He wondered how Merry could carry on such a conversation with Fritz in his broken English. But the other voice was too soft to be Fritz's, Uncle Tony soon realized.

There was silence as they came nearer. He could hear the scratching and bumping of something being dragged over the stones. Uncle Tony looked at his watch. It was one o'clock. Merry had not been away even the three hours he had felt sure she must take.

Suddenly Merry was standing beside him, the full moonlight showing the triumph in her face.

"Uncle Tony, I've brought Michael!"

Michael came from the shadow. "Hello, Uncle Tony. We'll soon have you out of this."

"Where's Fritz?"

"Fritz is on the Matterhorn. Don't you remember?"

"Oh!" Uncle Tony's smile fled. What could this boy and girl do to lift the rock? He shivered. The fire had gone out half an hour ago, and the moonlight, though beautiful, was cold.

Merry saw him shiver. She knelt down beside him, hunting in her pack for the extra sweaters and the thermos bottle. "Here's some hot milk, Uncle Tony."

She poured the milk out into a cup which Uncle Tony took with trembling fingers.

"Thanks," he smiled up at Merry. Turning to Michael, he began to explain how his feet were caught and what would have to be done to free them.

Michael nodded slowly. "Yes, I see. The thing to do is to raise the rock about four inches from this side."

Michael crouched low over Uncle Tony's legs and put his shoulder against the rock. He could not move it. He stepped back a bit, then picked up the rope, and tied it around the rock.

"See, Merry, I'm going to move back a bit and brace myself so I can get a good pull. When the stone moves, push this wedge in right here." He held out a three-cornered piece of rock. "Each time I pull, push this in as far as it will go. That should give a lift of three or four inches anyway."

"That will do the trick all right, Michael," said Uncle Tony admiringly, "if you can move it with the rope."

Merry dropped on her knees by the rock, holding the wedge ready. Michael took the rope in his hands and braced himself. "Count three, Uncle Tony," he called. "Then I'll pull."

Uncle Tony smiled at Michael's tone of confidence.

"One, two, and — three!"

Michael pulled on the rope. Bracing feet and knees till it seemed they would crack from the weight on them, he pulled and pulled.

Merry knelt by the rock, straining her eyes to see the opening between the stones where her wedge must go.

Michael loosed the rope. He stood limp, his limbs trembling from the strain put on them. Merry went over to him.

"Listen, Michael," Merry suggested. "Let Uncle Tony hold the wedge. I think he can reach it to put it in, and I'll pull with you."

Michael nodded, and Uncle Tony was given the wedge.

Michael and Merry braced themselves side by side, Michael's face stern and earnest, Merry's joyful at sharing in Uncle Tony's release.

"Count three, please," she cried, and Uncle Tony, putting into the numbers the lightness of heart he was far from feeling, counted, "One, two, three!"

The two pulled at the rope slowly. Michael was breathing heavily. Merry thought she would drop.

"Now," whispered Michael, "harder than ever — and don't let up for anything. It's got to give way."

They strained at the rope. Eagerly, Uncle Tony watched a thin strip of light widen as the rock that lay on top was separated from those it rested on. Leaning forward, he slipped the wedge in. Only a fraction at first — one inch, two inches, then the whole width of the wedge.

"Michael — I can't — any longer," Merry was almost crying, her breath coming in quick small gasps.

"Let go!" Uncle Tony cried.

The rope spun from their hands. Breathless, palms burning, Michael and Merry threw themselves on the earth beside Uncle Tony. "It's in," they panted.

They soon had their breath back and, though the rock was raised only a matter of inches, it was enough. Slowly, carefully, they worked Uncle Tony's feet free.

116

He sat up and began rubbing his ankles.

"How do they feel? Do they hurt, Uncle Tony?" Michael and Merry stood over him anxiously.

After a moment Uncle Tony laughed nervously. "They don't feel. It's as if they were asleep."

There was a pause. Then Michael said with decision, "Well, let's get back home. Then we'll see about them."

He tied the blanket over the wide slats of the sleigh and spread over the blanket the jackets and sweaters he and Merry had brought.

"Michael," said Uncle Tony, "leave some of the rope fastened to the back of the sleigh, so that one of you can hold it back on the way down."

"Right-o," Michael replied, working quickly.

Then, between them, they helped Uncle Tony onto the sleigh. With Merry holding the rope back to steady it, and Michael holding the curved runners, they guided the sleigh down the slope of the Gifferhorn, now gleaming with moonlight.

Passing the hay hut, they left a note on the door, to say thank you and that they would return the sleigh to-morrow.

Never had their chalet seemed so dear as when they sighted it at last. They pulled the sleigh up to the gate, and this time Uncle Tony, leaning on both of them, was able to limp into his room.

"Shall I go and get Frau Egli?" Michael asked.

Uncle Tony laughed. "No, thanks, Michael. My feet are getting some feeling into them now, and I hope by morning they'll be all right. I can manage quite well by myself. Good night, Rescue Team!"

Michael, murmuring good night, stumbled up the stairs and into bed with his clothes on. Merry's practical self had one last thought. Boiling some water, she filled the three hot-water bottles. Uncle Tony was in bed when she knocked on his door. Merry packed the bottles about his feet and he smiled at her gratefully.

"Good night," he said.

"Good morning," she laughed.

The moon had gone behind the line of mountains in the west and a faint sign of day was creeping over the valley when Merry got into bed.

Frau Egli, coming in the morning to get breakfast, wondered why the chalet was so still. Then, seeing the packs on the floor, the jackets and sweaters on a chair, she smiled to herself.

"The August moon," she said, placing her finger on her lips as she stole quietly back to her own chalet.

But no one in the village could account for Peter Wengli's sleigh standing before the chalet where Merry and Michael and Uncle Tony were staying.

Elizabeth Yates

ANIMALS CAN BE HEROES

ALEXANDER'S HORSE

ALEXANDER sat with his father, King Philip of Macedonia, watching the trainers deal with a great fiery horse from the plains of Thessaly. Alexander had seen many fine horses in his father's kingdom, but there were some things about this one that pleased him especially. He liked the mark on one shoulder like a bull's head that was the reason for the name Bucephalus. How proud the creature was! His body trembled with anger, and half a dozen men were needed to hold down that tossing head while a rider mounted.

Once loosed, the horse plunged and reared. He screamed with rage, and reached back at his rider with his teeth. He even struck furiously with his hoofs at his own shadow, as though the leaping black thing on the ground were also an enemy.

Man after man was thrown and torn or trampled by the raging horse until no one could be found who dared to mount him.

"The beast is useless," said King Philip at last to the horse dealer. "Take back your Bull's Head to your plains, Philonicus. I have no more men to waste on him."

But Alexander, the prince, could not bear to think that Macedonians would allow themselves to be overcome by a horse. He was at this time sixteen years old and athletic, and so spirited that when he walked he almost ran. He was so eager to be a hero that at each new victory of his father's he cried out, "Alas! What will there be left for me to conquer when I am grown?"

He was a student, too. The great Aristotle had come from Athens to be his teacher, and had acquainted the prince with some of the famous books of his country. The stories of Homer were Alexander's favorites. There he read of Achilles, the mightiest of the Greek heroes, fighting under the walls of Troy. Alexander's own mother claimed Achilles as an ancestor. She was a mountain princess, fierce and full of dreams, trusting to charms and magic. His father claimed as an ancestor the great Hercules, the strongest warrior in the world. Could one in whose veins were mixed the blood of the mighty Achilles and the great Hercules sit still while an animal triumphed over Macedonians?

Alexander leaped to his feet, his remarkable eyes shining. One eye was blue and one was brown, as though the gods had marked him from birth as different from ordinary men, but this strange coloring only added something unexpected to the charm of his healthy face and bright hair, waving up from his forehead.

"I'll ride him, Father!" he exclaimed.

King Philip eyed the boy, the hope of the kingdom, the only person alive who might continue his own victories, as well as succeed him on the throne. To allow the prince to ride such a horse was to place the whole future of Macedonia in danger. Yet only a fearless ruler would ever be able to hold that wild and unsettled country. The king still hesitated.

"I will stake the value of Bucephalus that I can ride him!" said Alexander, eager to master the proud and beautiful horse.

"Done," said Philip. But it was more than the breaking of a horse that was at stake. If his son failed to make good this boast, it was likely that he would fail in others. Gloomily, the king watched the scene before him.

The horse waited with heaving sides and rolling eyes to see what new enemy was approaching. Alexander went to his head. This was not dangerous, for Bucephalus was used to being led, and did not resist. Alexander stroked the horse's neck with a gentle hand. He calmed the animal with his voice. Then he turned Bucephalus to face the sun, for he alone had noticed the horse's fear of the shadow which had danced under his hoofs all morning, a shadow of strange shape because of the man on his back.

King Philip watched and approved. In the face of danger, his son was showing common sense as well as courage. Yet the king's breath came unevenly as he saw Alexander drop his cloak quietly and swing into the saddle. Immediately, Bucephalus whirled upward and the struggle between horse and rider began.

This time, the strange shadow was no longer dancing before the horse's eyes. The fight, while fierce, had lost something of its madness. Bucephalus reared and plunged, rushed forward, then stopped quickly, hoping to throw his rider. He whirled, leaped sideways, kicked, and reared again. But still the boy rode calmly, meeting every challenge with skill and courage, foreseeing each new move,

123

slowly gaining mastery as the animal under him tired. When, at last, Bucephalus bolted, and the plunging run steadied to a gallop, King Philip knew that the horse was conquered.

Instead of riding back at once to his father and the cheering crowd, Alexander showed that he knew how to follow up his victory as well as he had known how to prepare for it. The horse, which had at first run to please himself, was now running to please his new master. For miles and miles over the plains they rode, until Bucephalus was nearly worn out. It was a humble beast,

streaked with sweat and dust, that Alexander at last reined in before his father.

"My son!" cried Philip, greatly delighted. "You must find a kingdom worthy of you, for Macedonia will never hold you!"

From that day Bucephalus was Alexander's favorite horse. Anyone could lead him, but only Alexander could ride him. When his master approached, Bucephalus learned to kneel to be mounted. He was as fearless as his rider in war, and as jealous of his own honor. At the battle of Thebes, the horse was wounded but was unwilling that any other should be used in his place. For horses, as well as men, can be heroes in battles.

Bucephalus carried Alexander through half of Asia and proved himself a mighty swimmer of rivers. Once, some natives stole him from a pasture, and Alexander threatened to put the whole countryside to the sword if Bucephalus were not returned. When the animal was brought back unhurt in any way, his master loaded the very thieves with presents.

Yet only a charmed life could have protected Bucephalus forever. In the battle against the great Porus and his elephants in northern India, Alexander charged through a rain of spears. Some of them pierced the body of the horse, and he fell. His last act of devotion was to fall gently, so as not to hurt his royal rider.

Alexander grieved for the loss of Bucephalus as though a brother-in-arms had died. He was buried with full honors by the river where he fell. In his memory, Alexander founded a city there named Bucephala.

The city has long since disappeared and been forgotten, but Bucephalus is still remembered as the perfect battle horse, fierce against the enemy, but loving and faithful in all things to his master. The stories of the Middle Ages loved to tell of him, and to sing the praise of a horse as brave as any man in battle.

Elizabeth Coatsworth

DICK WHITTINGTON'S CAT

DICK GOES TO LONDON

MORE than five hundred years ago there was a boy named Dick Whittington. His father and mother died when he was too young to work, and so poor Dick was very badly off. He was quite glad to get the potato peelings to eat and a dry piece of bread now and then. More than that he did not often get, for the village where he lived was a very poor one, and the neighbors had little to give him.

Now the country folk in those days thought that the people of London were all fine ladies and gentlemen, and that there was singing and dancing all the day long, and that even the streets were paved with gold. Dick used to sit by and listen while all these strange tales of the splendor and wealth of London were told. They made him long to go and live there, and have plenty to eat and fine clothes to wear, instead of the rags and hard fare that fell to his lot in the country.

So one day, when a great wagon with eight horses stopped on its way through the village, Dick made friends with the wagoner and begged to be taken to London. The man felt sorry for poor Dick when he heard that he had no father or mother to take care of him, and saw how ragged the boy was. So he agreed to take Dick, and off they went.

How far it was and how many days the journey took I do not know, but in due time Dick found himself in the city which he had pictured to himself so grandly. But oh! how disappointed he was when he saw it. How dirty it was! And the people, how unlike the gay company, with music and singing, that he had dreamed of! He wandered up and down the streets, one after another, until he was tired out, but he did not find one that was paved with gold. He could see dirt in plenty, but none of the gold with which he had expected to fill his pockets.

Dick ran about till he was tired and it was growing dark. At last he sat down in a corner and fell asleep. When morning came, he was very cold and hungry. Though he asked everyone he met to help him, only one or two gave him a halfpenny to buy some bread. For two or three days he lived in the streets in this way, only just able to keep himself alive. Then he managed to get some work to do in a hayfield, and that kept him for a short time longer, till the haymaking was over.

After this he was as badly off as ever, and did not know where to turn. One day, in his wanderings, he lay down to rest in the doorway of a rich merchant whose name was Fitzwarren. Soon the cook in the house, an unkind, bad-

tempered woman, spied him and cried out to him to be off.
"Lazy rogue," she called him and said she'd throw some
dirty dishwater over him, boiling hot, if he didn't go.

Just then, however, Mr. Fitzwarren himself came home
to dinner. When he saw what was happening, he asked
Dick why he was lying there. "You're old enough to be
at work, my boy," he said. "I'm afraid you have a mind
to be lazy."

"Indeed, sir," replied Dick, "indeed, that is not so. I
have asked everywhere, but I have not been able to find
work since the haymaking."

Dick, poor fellow, was now so weak that, though he tried to stand, he had to lie down again, for it was more than three days since he had had anything to eat at all. The kind merchant gave orders for him to be taken into the house and given a good dinner. Then he was to be kept, to do what work he could to help the cook.

Dick would have been happy enough in this good family if it had not been for the bad-tempered cook, who did her best to make life hard for him. Night and morning she was forever scolding him. Nothing he did was good enough. It was "Look sharp here," and "Hurry up there," and there was no pleasing her. And many were the beatings he had from the broom handle or whatever else she had in her hand.

At last Miss Alice, Mr. Fitzwarren's daughter, heard how badly the cook was treating poor Dick. And she told the cook that she would quickly lose her place if she didn't treat him more kindly, for Dick had become quite a favorite with the family.

After that the cook behaved a little better, but Dick had still another hardship that he bore with difficulty. He slept in an attic where there were so many holes in the walls and floor that every night, as he lay in bed, the room was overrun with rats and mice. Sometimes he could hardly sleep a wink.

One day, when he had earned a penny for cleaning a

gentleman's shoes, he met a little girl with a cat in her arms and asked whether she would not sell it to him. "Yes, I will," she said, though the cat was such a good mouser that she was sorry to part with her. This just suited Dick, who kept pussy up in his attic, feeding her on scraps of his own dinner. In a little while he had no more trouble from the rats and mice. Puss saw to that, and Dick slept soundly every night.

Soon after this, Mr. Fitzwarren had a ship ready to sail. Now it was his custom to give all his servants a chance of good fortune when a ship was sent trading. So he called them all into the counting-house and asked them what they wished to send out.

They all had something that they were anxious to venture except poor Dick, who had neither money nor goods. For this reason he did not come with the rest. But Miss Alice guessed what was the matter, and ordered him to be called in. Then she said, "I will lay down some money for him out of my own purse, Father." But her father told her that would not do, for Dick must send something of his own.

When Dick heard this, he said, "I have nothing whatever but a cat, which I bought for a penny some time ago."

"Go, my boy, fetch your cat, then," said his master, "and let her go."

Dick went upstairs and fetched poor puss, but he sighed

as he gave her to the captain. "Now," he said, "I shall be kept awake all night by the rats and mice."

All the company but Miss Alice laughed at Dick's odd venture. She felt sorry for him and gave him some money to buy another cat.

This and other marks of kindness shown him by Miss Alice made the bad-tempered cook jealous of poor Dick. She began to treat him more cruelly than ever, and was always making game of him for sending his cat to sea.

"What do you think your cat will sell for?" she would ask. "As much money as would buy a stick to beat you with?"

At last poor Dick could not bear her bad temper and cruel treatment any longer, and he decided he would run away. So he made a bundle of his things — he hadn't many — and started out very early in the morning, on All Saints' Day, the first of November. He walked as far as Holloway. There he sat down to rest on a stone which to this day, they say, is called "Whittington's Stone," and began to ask himself which road he should take.

While he was wondering what he should do, the bells of Bow Church, in Cheapside, began to chime. As they rang, he fancied that they were singing over and over:

> "Turn again, Whittington,
> Lord Mayor of London."

"Lord Mayor of London!" said he to himself. "Why, to be sure, I would put up with almost anything now, to be Lord Mayor of London and ride in a fine coach when I grow to be a man! Well, I'll go back, and think nothing of the slapping and scolding of the cross old cook, since I am to be Lord Mayor of London at last."

So back he went, and he was lucky enough to get into the house and set about his work before the cook knew that he had been away.

A Cat and a King

But now you must hear what was happening to Puss all this while. The ship *Unicorn* was a long time at sea, and the cat made herself useful by disposing of many of the unwelcome rats on board.

At last the ship put into harbor on the coast of Barbary, where the only people are Moors. They had never before seen a ship from England, and flocked in numbers to see the sailors, whose different color and foreign dress were a great wonder to them. They were soon eager to buy the goods with which the ship was loaded, and samples were sent ashore for the King to see.

The King was so much pleased with these that he sent for the captain to come to the palace, and honored him with an invitation to dinner. But no sooner were they seated on their crossed legs, as is the custom there, on the fine rugs and carpets that covered the floor, than great numbers of rats and mice came running in, swarming over all the dishes, and helping themselves to all the good things to eat. The captain was amazed, and asked whether they didn't find such a pest most unpleasant.

"Oh yes," said they, "the rats are indeed a dreadful pest. The King would give half his treasure to be freed of them. They not only spoil his dinner, but they even attack him in his bed at night, so that a watch has to be kept while he is sleeping, for fear of them."

The captain was delighted to hear this, for he thought at once of poor Dick Whittington and his cat. "I have a creature on board ship," said he, "that would soon do for all these rats and mice if she were here."

Of course the King was immediately eager to own this wonderful animal.

"Bring her to me at once," he said. "If she will do what you say, I will load your ship with gold and jewels in exchange for her."

The captain, who knew his business, took care not to place too low a value on Dick's cat. He repeatedly told His Majesty how hard it would be to part with her, for, when she was gone, the rats might destroy the goods in the ship. To oblige the King, however, he said that he would fetch her.

135

"Oh, make haste, do!" cried the Queen. "I, too, am impatient to see this dear creature."

Off went the captain, while another dinner was prepared. He got back to the palace with Puss under his arm just in time to see the carpet covered with rats and mice once again. When Puss saw them, she didn't wait to be told what to do, but jumped out of the captain's arms, and in no time had laid almost all the rats and mice dead at her feet, while the few that were left had run off to their holes in fright.

The King was delighted to get rid of such a terrible plague so easily. The Queen asked that the animal which had done them such a service should be brought to her. The captain called out, "Puss, puss, puss," and she came running to him. Then he presented her to the Queen, who was rather afraid at first to touch her. However, when the captain called her "Pussy, pussy," and began to stroke her, the Queen also ventured to touch her and cried "Putty, putty," in imitation of the captain, for she had not learned to speak English. He then put the cat on

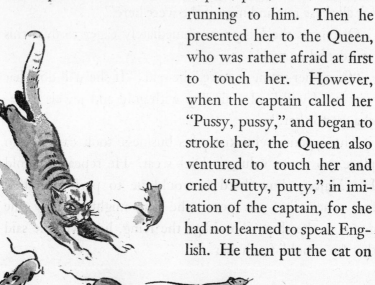

the Queen's lap, where she purred and played with Her Majesty's hand and was soon asleep.

The King now began bargaining with the captain for the whole ship's cargo. Then, having seen what Puss could do and learning that her kittens would soon stock the whole country and keep it free from rats, he offered the captain ten times as much for the cat as for all the rest of the goods, a sum which the captain gladly accepted.

The *Unicorn* then sailed away from Barbary, and, after a fair voyage, reached London again with the precious load of gold and jewels safe and sound.

Early one morning, as soon as Mr. Fitzwarren had come to his counting-house and settled himself at his desk, there came a knock at the door.

"Who's there?" said he.

"A friend," replied a voice. "I come with good news of your ship, the *Unicorn*."

The merchant hastily opened the door, and who should be there but the ship's captain and the mate, bearing a chest of jewels and a bill of lading. When Mr. Fitzwarren had looked this over, he lifted his eyes and thanked heaven for sending him such a prosperous voyage.

The honest captain next told him all about the cat, and showed him the rich present the King had sent in exchange. As happy over Dick's good fortune as he had been over his own, Mr. Fitzwarren called to his servants to bring Dick.

"Go fetch him, and we'll tell him of his fame.
Pray call him Mr. Whittington by name."

The servants, some of them, hesitated at this, and said that so great a treasure was too much for a lad like Dick. But Mr. Fitzwarren showed himself the good man that he was by refusing to deprive the boy of a single penny. "God forbid!" he cried. "It's all his own, and he shall have it, to a farthing."

He then ordered them again to send up Dick, who at the moment was cleaning pots and pans for the cook. Dick tried to excuse himself from coming into the room because he was black with dirt, but the merchant insisted, and had a chair set for him. Dick began to think they must be making game of him, and begged them not to play tricks on a poor boy, but to let him go back to his work.

"Indeed, Mr. Whittington," said the merchant, "we are all quite in earnest with you. I rejoice as will you at the news that these gentlemen have brought. The captain of the *Unicorn* has sold your cat to the King of Barbary, and brings you in return more riches than I possess in the whole world. May you long enjoy them!"

Mr. Fitzwarren then told the men to open the great treasure they had brought, saying, "There is nothing more now for Whittington to do but to put it in some place of safety."

138

Poor Dick hardly knew how to behave for joy. He begged his master to take what part of it he pleased, since he owed it all to his kindness.

"No, no," answered Mr. Fitzwarren, "this all belongs to you. I have no doubt that you will use it well."

Dick next begged his mistress, and then Miss Alice, to accept a part of his good fortune, but they would not. At the same time they told him what great joy they felt at his good fortune. But he was far too kind-hearted to keep the money all to himself. So he made a present to the captain, the mate, and the rest of Mr. Fitzwarren's servants, even to his old enemy, the bad-tempered cook.

After this, Mr. Fitzwarren advised him to send for a tailor and get himself dressed like a gentleman, and told him he was welcome to live in the house till he could provide himself with a better.

When Whittington's face was washed, his hair curled, and he was dressed in a smart suit of clothes, he was just as handsome and fine a young man as any who visited at Mr. Fitzwarren's. So thought fair Alice Fitzwarren, who had once been so kind to him and looked upon him with pity. Now she felt, secretly, that she would like him for her sweetheart. She felt so the more, no doubt, because Whittington was always thinking what he could do to please her.

Mr. Fitzwarren soon saw which way the wind blew, and before long offered to join them in marriage. To this they both readily agreed and a day for the wedding was set. They were attended to church by the Lord Mayor, the court of aldermen, the sheriffs, and a great number of the richest merchants in London, whom they afterwards treated to a magnificent feast.

History tells us that Mr. Whittington and his lady lived in great splendor and were very happy. They had several children. He became Sheriff of London, and thrice Lord Mayor, and was knighted by Henry V.

After the King's conquest of France, Sir Richard Whittington entertained the King and Queen at dinner at the Mansion House in so grand a manner that the King said, "Never had Prince such a subject!" To which Sir Richard replied, "Never had subject such a Prince!"

Flora Annie Steel

140

BRAVE TONY

THIS is a story of San Sebastian on the northern coast of Spain. Like many other towns, San Sebastian had to deal with the problem of a stray dog. The only place this dog could call home was the narrow, dark passage running between two rows of deserted houses on the edge of town. There he often lay on the damp, mossy flagstone walk, catching a wink of sleep, but disappearing in a flash at the sound of a footstep.

The dog ventured out into the town only when it was dark. Like some wild animal, he prowled up one street and down another, always avoiding the lamp lights and keeping in the shadows. Nosing the lids off garbage cans, he would hunt through the contents for a scrap of food or a bone. But times were so hard in Spain since the Civil War that there was rarely much left for the garbage cans.

Many stories sprang up about the mysterious appearances of this strange animal. They were never proved, but the people of San Sebastian believed them and hesitated to go into the streets after dark for fear of meeting him. However, some who did happen to catch a glimpse of him, saw in his coat, once silver, but now matted and dirty, proof that he must once upon a time have been a fine dog.

Perhaps it was this that led some people to believe that he was another unfortunate of the Civil War. Some said he had been a Red Cross dog or a message carrier. Others added to the tale and insisted that he had been wounded in action and had been unable to get back to the army, and that he had since wandered from place to place, looking for his former master, until finally he had settled down in San Sebastian. He was usually called Tony, although nobody could say why.

These were the tales that little Lolita liked best to hear from her father as they sat by the open fire in their tavern.

"Tell me, Papa," she would urge, "about the brave war dog." And he would tell her the stories, over and over, until she fell fast asleep.

One night in the early spring, when Lolita went to the kitchen door to call in her cat, there was a clatter outside. The lid of the garbage can hit the ground and spun away over the stones. A head flew up and a gray form disappeared in the shadows.

142

Lolita ran through the hall to her father. "Papa! Papa!" she called.

He looked up from his paper as she ran in. Her blue eyes shone.

"What is it, Lolita?" he asked.

"I've seen him!" she exclaimed. "I've seen him!"

"Who, child? What do you mean?"

"Tony, the brave war dog!"

"Nonsense!" replied her father. "You've heard so much about him that now you imagine you've seen him!"

But Lolita was sure she had seen the dog. Before she went to bed, she set a bowl full of milk on the flagstone just outside the kitchen door. The next morning the milk was gone, and the dish was overturned.

Each night after that, the dog made the tavern his first stop. And each morning Lolita found the bowl licked clean and overturned. Evening after evening, she sat out on the steps, her cat purring softly in her lap, hoping to see the dog again. Sometimes she called, "Tony, here, Tony," but never again did she see him. He always seemed to wait until she had gone to bed before coming to get his milk.

One day, when Lolita and her father were out walking, they came on a crowd gathered in the street. In the center of the crowd, lying on the ground, was a big dog. A rope was around his neck. He snarled at the men who were trying to hold him. But the more he struggled, the tighter became the rope around his neck. It was choking him.

Suddenly Lolita saw him. "Papa! Papa!" she cried out. "Look! It's Tony! Please make them stop hurting him!"

The father shook his head. "There's nothing I can do, Lolita, child," he replied. "They're the dog-catchers!" He took her hand. "Come on, dear," he urged, "we must be getting home!"

But Lolita twisted free from her father and pushed through the crowd. People tried to stop her. They reached for her, but she shook herself free.

"Come back, child!" they cried in horror. "It's a mad dog! Can't you see? Stay back!"

Lolita paid no attention to these warnings. She made her way through the crowd and flung herself down at the side of the dog. He was still fighting against the rope around his neck.

"Poor Tony! My poor, brave Tony!" she repeated softly, as she stroked his head. The dog quieted down instantly. The rope loosened as he lay still, his big brown eyes staring at her.

The dog-catchers stood by, amazed at the sight of this child petting the fierce dog which had frightened the whole town for months. No one dared make a move for fear the girl would come to harm.

"Papa," she pleaded over and over again, "I want him

144

for my own. If the dog-catchers take him, he will die. I can make him get well. Please let me have him."

Her father tried to reason with her, but Lolita was determined to have Tony for her pet. Finally, on condition that her father would be responsible for the dog, Lolita was allowed to take him.

Tony went quietly home with Lolita and her father, but there, almost immediately, he became ill. A doctor was called. There was no hope for Tony, he said. But not for an instant did Lolita give up hope. He was her hero — this brave war dog. For weeks she nursed him. Slowly Tony grew better. Then suddenly they realized that the dog was blind.

But lack of sight did not keep him from learning his way around the tavern and then around the little town of San Sebastian. He was a changed dog. The scars that had given rise to stories about his past disappeared as his coat became smooth and silvery.

Tony became a real part of the life at the tavern. He was the first to meet guests. His tail wagged a welcome. His cold wet nose was always ready to snuggle into a palm.

At regular times during the night Tony left Lolita's room, of his own accord. From door to door, from floor to floor, he went through the entire house, like a night watchman making his rounds.

Every morning at half-past seven, as regular as an alarm clock, Tony got up, stretched, yawned, and was off on his last round. This time he stopped at each room where the guest had to rise at that hour. He pawed lightly on the door and barked softly. If no answer came, he kept it up until finally a sleepy voice called out from inside, "All right, Tony! All right." Then he would go on to the next room.

Most important in Tony's life was his devotion to Lolita. He took her to school in the morning, his head

up, his tail wagging proudly. And he knew right on the dot when to get back to meet her. In spite of his blindness, he never crossed the street until the traffic had stopped and the way was clear.

That was Tony's new life. True, it was a life of darkness, but it was also a life of usefulness and happiness.

One day, a big new ocean liner was due to arrive. This was a great event for San Sebastian. Everybody in town who could possibly leave his work went down to the dock to watch the ship come in. Tony went too, with Lolita in her gay Spanish dress, and some of her friends.

At the dock, Tony stretched out in the hot sun to snatch a wink or two of sleep before the boat arrived. As soon as he was comfortably settled, the children started a game of leap frog over him. In disgust, he moved farther away and tried it again. Soon he slept peacefully, the dock under him swaying gently with the roll of the ocean.

The far-off, deep-throated toot of a whistle sounded as the ship came in sight. The crowd moved to the edge of the dock and shaded their eyes with their hands as they watched the liner come nearer.

Suddenly there was a commotion. A splash! A scream! Tony was up instantly. He pushed his way through the crowd. He ran from one child to another hunting for Lolita. She was not to be found. Throwing his head high, he listened. Through the noise of the crowd, he caught, ever so faintly, the frightened cries of Lolita, struggling in the water.

He jumped and hit the water with a dull splash. For a second he was almost stunned. Salt water filled his ears and his mouth. Then he recovered and started swimming. At last Tony's jaws locked tight on Lolita's dress.

People whistled and called from the dock, urging him in. "Here, boy! Come on, Tony! Here, this way!"

But Tony knew he could not count on making the dock from which he had jumped. It was too high for him. Instead, he started to swim around it, making for the shore.

The crowd watched him turn. Boats, hastily launched, began pulling out to head him off. But on and on Tony swam, aiming by instinct for that shore he couldn't even see. Lolita's fingers clutched tight into his coat. Finally, his feet touched bottom and he struggled to the sandy beach.

"Tony," whispered Lolita as the big dog dragged her up on the beach. "My brave Tony!"

Tony licked her once across the face. Perhaps he was remembering the day some two years before when she had rescued him. Then, in joy and satisfaction, he shook himself from the tip of his nose to the tip of his tail, throwing water everywhere as the crowd surrounded them.

Don Lang

THE SILVER STAR

On my tenth birthday I received the most exciting and most prized gift of my life. That morning my father said, "Selim, come to the market-place with me."

Little guessing what was in store for me, I followed him, and we walked along the road till we came to the busy market-place. In Arabia we have few automobiles, and our means of transportation are very limited.

After we arrived in the market, what do you think my father gave me? The brightest little camel you can imagine! She had sparkling intelligent eyes and clean silky hair, and she was as gentle as the kitten in your corner. I fell in love with her at once.

"Oh, Father," I cried, "I thank you. I shall call her Zeta."

He nodded agreement. "My son," he said, "be good to this animal, and you will never be without a friend."

I took Zeta home with me with pride, and my father and I soon built a shelter for her. I spent many happy days with her. We roamed the hills and sand dunes and grew to love each other like brother and sister. I taught her many tricks: to wait for me while I hunted and did errands, to lie on the ground till I was properly mounted, and to fetch things which I left at our secret hiding places. She was very intelligent and never forgot what she had learned. She grew to be so beautiful that I received many offers from merchants who wished to buy her, but I would not part with her for any price.

Zeta's eyes were covered by long, beautiful lashes which protected her keen sight from sun glare and drifting sand. Her nostrils were not open, like those of other animals, but were narrow slits, very much like those of a sheep. They could be closed tightly to protect her from the terrible sand storms of the desert. Her foot had two toes, covered with a cushion-like pad which spread out under her weight and prevented her from going down too deeply into the sand. Her underlip was covered with brushlike hair which strained the sand out of her drinking water.

Her hump was filled with fat and moisture so that she could live without water longer than most animals. Some of the stories about the ability of the camel to do without food and water for a long time are not true. Without food and water, a camel can live for only a few days.

For five happy years the ties of affection between Zeta and myself grew stronger and stronger. Then our land was attacked by the fierce tribes of Berber warriors on our north. I volunteered to help defend our country. My hardest task was leaving Zeta. On my last day at home, she followed me wherever I went. With tears in my eyes, I shut her in the shed and went away.

Because of my knowledge of the country, I was used as a scout to spot enemy positions and report them to my chief. I worked at this dangerous task for some months. I often thought of Zeta, waiting at home for the time when I should return. One day it suddenly occurred to me that since we had shared everything in time of peace, why should we not share the fortunes of war? I reported my idea to the commander, who gave me leave to fetch my beloved camel.

What joy there was in our reunion! She whinnied and neighed as if to tell me of the sadness she had felt at our separation. Happily we rode back to the camp, and Zeta became the talk of our troop because of her speed, courage, and intelligence.

One dark night I was given the task of finding the enemy positions. The Berbers had advanced deeply into our territory, and our commander had decided on a heavy counter-attack. I mounted Zeta and we were soon traveling swiftly across the silent sands.

After a few hours, I spotted the fires of the enemy. Leaving Zeta at a safe distance, I went in on foot as close as I dared. I carefully noted the position and the numbers of the troops. Suddenly I heard a shout and the crack of a rifle. A sharp-eyed guard had spotted me.

I ran back to my faithful camel and quickly mounting her, I sped away. Glancing back over my shoulder, I saw a group of Berbers in hot pursuit. I urged my animal on, knowing that her speed would make her more than a match for the beasts of my enemies. Suddenly I felt a sharp and terrible pain in my shoulder. I had been struck by a bullet fired by one of their crack shots. I fell forward on Zeta's neck but managed to hang on till we had safely outrun the enemy and escaped in the darkness. Then I fell off Zeta onto a heap of cool sand.

I do not know how long I lay there, but when I came to, it was still dark, and Zeta was close by, trying to be of some help. I scarcely knew what to do. I could not possibly mount Zeta and ride her back to camp, but it was essential that the commander receive before dawn the information I had gained. Suddenly, I had an inspiration. I took out a pad and pencil and wrote down the important information I had gathered, and fastened the paper to Zeta's saddle-bag.

"Go back to camp," I ordered.

She looked at me sadly for a moment, but made no move.

"Zeta, did you not hear me? Go back to camp!"

Her intelligent eyes told me that she knew what I wished of her, but she shook her head, as if to say, "Though you order me away, I will not leave you alone while you are hurt."

"Zeta, return. I, Selim, command it."

Again she shook her head and pressed her soft nose in my face. In anger I raised my fist and struck her for the first time in my life.

"Go!" I shouted.

She looked at me in hurt astonishment and grief for a moment, and then she turned and galloped away.

After a few hours dawn came, and I heard the beat of flying hoofs. Looking up, I saw some men from my own troop approaching. They set me on one of their camels and took me back to camp.

There I asked to be taken directly to the commander.

"Did you get my information?" I asked him.

"Yes, Selim. Thanks to you and your camel, we surprised the enemy and won a complete victory."

"And Zeta? How is she?"

"She was pretty low when I left her, Selim."

"What! Is she hurt?"

"Yes. One of the bullets that were fired at you last night must have struck her."

Before I would let the doctor attend to my wound, I hurried over to see my poor Zeta. She was lying on a patch of straw and made a weak sound as I came in. In spite of her own serious wound, my faithful animal had followed my orders.

"Will she die?" I asked the doctor anxiously.

"She is very weak, but I think she will recover, Selim," he said.

Happily I let him bandage me. As the days passed, Zeta and I recovered slowly together.

In recognition of my services, I was awarded the decoration of the Silver Star, the highest honor of our army. However, I pinned the decoration on Zeta's saddle, that we might share the honor, as we share everything.

Samuel Meyer

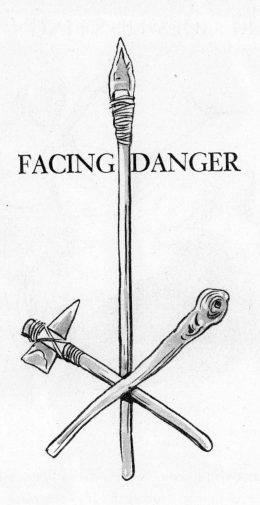

FACING DANGER

TURI GOES HUNTING

ALONE IN THE WOODS

I WANT you to come with me on a long journey into the past, a journey across the sea to a place we now call France. There we shall find Turi, a boy who lived twenty thousand years ago, and his sister, Mee-Na, and their father, Ka-Gora, the great hunter.

Today, in France, you can see the place where Turi used to live. You can stand in the rock shelter, high on the side of a cliff, that was Turi's home. On the walls of a deep, dark cavern you can see the pictures of animals that Turi drew. You can see the marks of Turi's feet in the clay floor, and hold in your hands the flint tools the boy used.

In the valley below, Turi hunted great mammoths, and wolves, and reindeer, and the hairy rhinoceros. You will see a winding river flowing through this wide, green valley. On one side of the valley is a towering limestone cliff. High up in that cliff you can see shallow caves. In those caves, twenty thousand years ago, glowed the hearth fires of the Cro-Magnon people — a race of men that looked something like the white men of today.

Before dawn one morning, in one of those rock shelters, the boy Turi stirred in his bed of skins. He threw aside his skins and shivered, as he stood tall, straight, and bronzed, in the chilly morning air. He pushed back his blond hair from his eyes, and looked to see if his family were awake. But, no, they all seemed to be sleeping. Quickly, he took up his little spear and his club, then looked around the fire for some scraps of meat. As he stooped, his sister, Mee-Na, opened her eyes and started up when she saw him.

"Turi!" she whispered. "Where are you going?"

"Ssssh!" he answered. "My father will not take me, so I am going to hunt by myself!"

"Don't be silly!" Mee-Na protested. "You are too young. Some cave bear will gobble you up!"

Turi laughed. "What do girls know about hunting!" he said. "I'll show my father I can hunt! I have a sharp spear, and a club, and a strong arm!" Without another word he moved toward the edge of the cliff, stepped over it, and was on his way down to the valley.

The morning mists were thick about him as Turi made his way through the tall grass toward the trees that lined the banks of the river. The grass was wet with dew, and the air was chilly. Clad only in his girdle of wolf-skin, Turi shivered. Above the distant hills, a pale sun was rising. Beneath its rays, the mists of the valley grew thin. Now Turi could see the trees, and, beyond them, the river. His heart beat faster, for adventure lay all around him.

Turi walked slowly along the river bank, his club and his spear clutched tightly in his hands. For an instant the air cleared of mist and Turi saw a huge brown mass in front of him.

"A boulder!" he whispered to himself. "I can hide behind that and catch some small animal that comes to the river to drink!"

He moved forward through the long grass. The mist whirled by, and, to Turi's horror, the boulder moved!

158

What he had thought was a big rock was really a huge rhinoceros!

Turi was frozen with fear. The rhino looked at him with one little red eye. Slowly, like a moving mountain, it turned to face him. Turi tried to remember that he was the son of a mighty hunter, but still his knees shook. He was so little, and the rhino so big. Here, in the open, the rhino could crush him to death in an instant.

Turi thought of the trees. If he could get among them, where the rhino could not run, he might escape. Like a flash, he turned and ran. With a grunt, the rhino moved heavily after him, the ground shaking under his feet. To Turi the trees seemed far away. The long grass clutched at his flying feet and the rhino was close behind.

Turi went faster and faster. He threw away his club, then his spear. The rhino was almost upon him! With a great bound, the boy leaped into the shelter of the nearest trees. His flying feet slid in the mud. Breathless, he fell on his face. There was a mighty crash close behind him.

Turi sat up slowly. He could not believe that he was still alive. Then he stared, amazed. The rhinoceros was pawing fiercely at the wet clay beneath its feet, throwing up great showers of mud, but its body was not moving. The rhino was caught fast between two trees!

Like a grown hunter, Turi thought first of his weapons. He ran back to where he had dropped his spear and club. The thongs that bound the stones to their wooden shafts were wet — and loose. But he could not stop for that now. They were useless against the thick hide of the rhino anyway.

Turi stopped to think. What would his father do now? The beast must not be allowed to escape. Ah! He had an idea!

Quickly Turi laid down his weapons, and stripped off his skin girdle. At the edge of the trees he found a large stone. He laid down the skin, and rolled the stone onto it. To the four corners of the skin he tied his girdle thong. Stooping, he put his head through the loop. When he rose, the great stone was hanging from his neck.

Close by the struggling rhino was a large tree wrapped around with vines. If he could climb those vines, Turi thought, and drop the stone on the rhino's head, the beast would bother him no more. Slowly he staggered toward the tree, bracing himself against the weight of the stone. Seizing the vines, he pulled himself up.

Turi reached a branch of the tree which stretched out over the rhino's head. On hands and knees, the boy moved out along the bough. The stone was heavy. He panted for breath as he inched along carefully. When he was almost over the rhino, Turi lifted the stone from its sling. Suddenly the bough cracked. Turi grabbed at it with one hand. There was a dreadful tearing sound as the bough

gave way, and Turi, the stone, and the branch crashed down on the rhino below.

Slowly Turi sat up and looked around him. The branch of the tree lay across the rhino's neck. The beast had slid down in the mud and did not move.

Turi got up and he was a little afraid — not of the rhino, for the rhino was dead. He was afraid his father would be angry if he learned that his young son had been so careless as to let himself be nearly killed. He must get away from this place as quickly as he could. He snatched up his spear and club and set off through the woods.

With the help of chance, he had killed the much-feared hairy rhinoceros. But he dared not tell his father. To prove himself a hunter, he must kill some small creature, taking no risks that a boy of his size should not take.

A MIGHTY HUNTER

All day he hunted with no success. Once he sighted a family of reindeer, which made such good eating, but they were too fast for him. Later, he narrowly escaped the fierce attack of some wild boars.

Finally, it began to grow dark. It was too late to hunt, and Turi was far from home, and a little bit afraid. Now he was almost running. He must get out of those woods before darkness fell.

Suddenly his toe struck a moss-covered log. He lost his balance and fell flat on his face. A small furry creature slid from under his body and darted away. It was a baby wolf. Turi scrambled to his feet. With all his might he threw the flint spear-head. The stone struck the animal at the back of the head and it rolled over in the grass and lay still. Turi seized his prize. Now he had something to show, something they could eat. Slinging it over his shoulder, he marched homeward once more, humming the hunting song of the tribe as he went.

In the distance, Turi could see the hearth fire of his home high on the cliff ahead. The sun had gone down, and all around was silence. Turi hurried. Suddenly his heart skipped a beat. He heard nothing, yet he had a strange feeling that he was being followed. He looked fearfully behind him and saw something dark moving against the short grass. Turi hurried faster. The Thing moved faster. It was drawing closer. Turi wanted to run, but he knew that would do no good. He must not show fear, or the creature would attack. Once more he looked back. Now he saw it was a wolf! What could he do? It was probably the mother of the baby wolf he had killed.

For a moment Turi thought of dropping the dead animal he was carrying, but then his day of hunting would have been for nothing. He dared not go home with nothing to show, for even if his father were not angry, he would laugh at Turi for thinking he could hunt.

Stumbling through the growing darkness, Turi reached the slope below the cliff. Faster and faster he hurried. Closer and closer crept the wolf. The path was steep, and Turi was tired. His legs ached. His arms ached. He was terribly afraid. Turi, panting as he climbed, shouted as loudly as he could. Perhaps someone would hear and come to help him. For an instant he saw the outline of Mee-Na's head and shoulders as she looked down at him from the cave. He scrambled madly upward, scattering loose stones with his feet. Behind him was the wolf, and each instant he expected it to spring. Then he reached the top of the cliff and fell into the mouth of the cave. At that instant the wolf leaped upon him!

Turi fell on his face, and the wolf was thrown to one side. The next instant, the wolf gave a sharp cry and a howl of pain, as Mee-Na thrust a flaming brand from the fire into the open jaws. The wolf, snarling, jumped backward. Then, without a sound, it leaped for Mee-Na's throat. With all her might, Mee-Na brought the heavy brand crashing down upon its head. The wolf rolled over — dead!

Now there was a sound of someone climbing the trail to the cave, and Turi's mother came in sight. She saw Turi lying on the ground, covered with mud and blood. She saw the wolf lying dead.

"My brave boy!" she cried. "He killed a wolf and saved his sister's life!"

Turi wanted to explain, but Mee-Na put her finger to her lips, signaling him to keep silent.

Now there was a shout from below. Turi's father came climbing up the rocks, a huge piece of meat across his shoulders, and a happy smile on his face.

"Well!" he exclaimed, as he saw the wolf. "What's been going on here?"

"It's Turi," his wife explained. "Turi fought the wolf and saved Mee-Na's life."

Ka-Gora looked at Turi, and laughed proudly. "Come here, my son," he said. "Let us take a look at the mighty hunter!"

Turi went slowly to his father. He was ashamed. How could he take praise for something his sister had done? He made up his mind. He would not do it, even if his father punished him.

"No!" he cried. "I did not kill the wolf. Mee-Na did it, and saved my life."

Then Turi looked at his father in amazement. Instead of scolding him, his father laughed again.

"So you did not kill the wolf!" he shouted. "Never mind, mighty hunter! What is a wolf to one who, all by himself, killed a rhino!"

Turi's heart leaped high. His father knew! He was not angry!

"How did you know?" he murmured.

"How did I know?" repeated his father. "Did I not find your footprints in the mud around the rhino? Did I not find your torn girdle wrapped around a stone? Now, thanks to my young son, we have plenty to eat for many days to come. And as for Mee-Na — come here, daughter. You, too, are worthy of your father. And when you skin this wolf, be sure to make another girdle for your brother. Soon he will go with me on the hunt."

Henry Lionel Williams

THE HERRING CART

EVERY day, after school, Hendrik sold herrings on the Queen's Bridge. This is only one of the many small bridges that span the canals in Holland, but it is an amusing bridge all the same. Trolley cars make a stop right in the middle of it, cars and bicycles crowd it at lunch hours, and brightly painted boats take their way beneath it on the water. There is always something interesting to look at.

Besides, it's a very good place for business. On the western end of the bridge, Mr. Cornelius sells flowers. On the eastern end, Hendrik's herring cart has a special stand. Mr. William van der Hope, the policeman, having nothing to sell, has his place opposite the flower seller.

"Mr. van der Hope is rather fat for a policeman," Hendrik thought one afternoon, when he set up his herring cart on the bridge. "Perhaps he eats too big a breakfast."

Usually Hendrik thought nice things about Mr. van der Hope, for he admired him very much, but today everything was going wrong. He forgot to say "Hello" to Mr. Cornelius, and he didn't care how his own cart looked. Yet the cart was in perfect order. White and spotless, it decorated the bridge. Its sign read in proud letters:

HENDRIK'S HEALTHY HERRINGS

166

There was no better herring cart in town. Salt and spices stood ready for use, and a big bowl of chopped onions smelled inviting. The herrings themselves, those delicious, silver-shining, Dutch butter-herrings, were, of course, inside the cart on ice.

If Hendrik had thought to eat one of his wonderful herrings himself, he might have cheered up. For a herring is the best thing to eat a Hollander can imagine. He usually enjoys about five a day. He has one the first thing in the morning to butter the stomach for all the good things to come. He has number two at the beginning of a hearty lunch, and number three to cheer him up in the afternoon. Number four puts him in a good humor for dinner, and the fifth and last herring comes as the happy ending of a beautiful day.

Every day, at the stroke of five, Mr. William van der Hope, being of course a good Hollander, would come over to Hendrik's Healthy Herrings to have his "cheer-up"

fish. And here he came this afternoon, taking long, confident policeman's steps. He saw at once that Hendrik was unhappy. So, instead of starting a little chat as usual, he took hold of Hendrik's thick hair and asked, "What's wrong, my boy?"

"Plenty!" said Hendrik.

"I should like to hear everything," the policeman insisted.

"All right," Hendrik sighed. "It's the same as last week. I slept during lessons again. The teacher was very angry. He said I should give up the herring business and do my home-work during the day like other children. Otherwise I might as well leave school and give up the idea of building ships when I grow up. I don't know what to do, Mr. van der Hope. I have to sell herrings to pay for school and then I'm too tired to do home-work at night."

Mr. van der Hope shook his head over the sad news. After a while, he said, "My herring, please. I always get ideas after I have had a silver fish."

Hendrik went to work at once. He cleaned the herring with a sharp knife, put salt and spices on it and plenty of onions for flavor. He handled it so skillfully that every Hollander passing by felt his mouth water. So did Mr. van der Hope.

When Hendrik was through, the policeman took the herring by the tail and with a jerk pulled it into two parts.

168

He then held it up in the air like a bunch of grapes, closed his eyes, and let one part after another slowly disappear into Mr. van der Hope's mouth.

"Ah!" he said. "A herring makes life worth living. And," he went on, "I have just thought of something which might prove useful to you." His face took on an important expression.

"Listen, Hendrik," he began. "We are looking for a thief who is hard to catch. He has stolen hundreds of pounds of cheese at the Gouda cheese market, and the merchants are very angry. We went after this thief, but he is a sly fellow and disappears like a mouse in a hole. To interest all Hollanders in catching this public enemy, the merchants of Gouda have collected three thousand guilders. Whoever catches the cheese thief will get that sum. But he must give part of the money to the clever person who has told him where the thief may be found."

"And you think, Mr. van der Hope, that I might be able to find him?" Hendrik interrupted.

"Why not?" the policeman replied. "A boy keeping his eyes open in the streets (here Mr. van der Hope cleared his throat) might be the lucky one. Look at me, Hendrik." (Mr. van der Hope came closer and spoke as friend to friend.) "I am going to give you some inside information. The thief we want doesn't look like a Hollander at all. He is black-haired and thin, but he likes

herrings as only a Dutchman does. He has a peculiar
habit in eating them. He will take the herring by its tail
fin and whirl it three times through the air before taking
his first bite. Isn't it strange?" Mr. van der Hope asked.

"It surely is," Hendrik thought, but had no time to
answer. The siren of a fire-truck was heard, and Mr. van
der Hope had to clear the bridge of traffic.

Hendrik was left to his own thoughts. He stared into
the clouds. He was thinking, "I am just a boy selling
herrings on the bridge, but I have a policeman's friendship and help. Why shouldn't I win the three thousand
guilders? I know all the small streets and places nobody
else ever saw. There is a back yard where it smells of fish
all the time. It is filled with barrels and it's dirty and
dark. Perhaps just now the thief is hiding there."

"How about a herring?" a customer interrupted
Hendrik's dreams. When the man had his fish and had
gone away, Hendrik tried to keep on thinking. But all
of a sudden, it occurred to him that he had no time to
look around for a thief. It was a good chance for some
other boy — not for him. He had to attend school and
sell herrings on the bridge afterward. He felt like crying
but didn't, for Mr. van der Hope might have seen him.

Time went by. Hendrik and Mr. van der Hope never
had another conversation about the thief who whirled the
herring. The policeman avoided the subject. Perhaps

he was ashamed of himself for telling Hendrik about a problem the whole police force could not solve. Hendrik's herring cart still stood at its place every day, and Hendrik slept through lessons once in a while. Sometimes, on his way to school or coming home with his herring cart, Hendrik would give a quick look down small and dark streets in the hope of seeing a strange man. But when fall came he forgot about that, too.

One day, waiting for customers, Hendrik had his jacket buttoned up against the chilly air. He was dreaming about the ships he would build some day.

"How about a herring?" Someone interrupted his thoughts.

Hendrik came back to earth and put up the lid of his cart to pick out a fish. He caught sight of the man in front of him. He was thin and black-haired. All of a sudden Hendrik realized, "This man doesn't look like a Hollander at all. But it cannot be the thief," he said to himself. "He wouldn't dare to come to the bridge in bright daylight." He looked around for Mr. van der Hope, who was usually near by. But Mr. van der Hope was nowhere in sight.

Hendrik went on thinking as he finished preparing the fish with salt and spices and onions. Hendrik watched closely as the man took the herring and caught it by the tail. He held it high up in the air and — began whirling it — once, twice, three times! Hendrik held his breath.

172

A moment later he grasped the man's head and forced it down into the bowl of chopped onions.

"Help, help, I've got him!" he cried.

The cheese thief freed himself easily from Hendrik's grasp and tried to run away, but in vain. He was nearly blind, for the onions made him weep. He was still weeping when Mr. van der Hope finally came and put handcuffs on him.

Hendrik was treated like a hero for at least a week. He was praised in the newspapers, his classmates admired him, and the teacher said he was a brave boy. Hendrik himself wasn't quite so sure. "It was mostly luck," he said.

But Hendrik is now enjoying the reward of three thousand guilders. His "Healthy Herrings" cart is stored away in the attic. He can do his home-work in the afternoon and will be a shipbuilder one day.

On Sundays, he goes to call on his friend, Mr. van der Hope, on the Queen's Bridge. After a chat, both of them go over to a new herring cart which has Hendrik's old place on the bridge and have a "cheer-up" fish. Before eating it, they take the herring by its tail fin, whirl it three times through the air, and wink at each other like old friends.

Luis

ROSIE AND THE LION

THERE lived in England, not so long ago, a very famous lion. His name was Monarch. He was a big handsome fellow with a bold head and a magnificent mane. There lived also in England, at the same time, a girl by the name of Rose Purchase.

Monarch came of a long line of jungle kings. Rose Purchase came of a long line of lion trainers. Her father, Captain Purchase, was a lion trainer, and her grandfather had been one also. The fact that she was a girl, and that such a thing as a girl lion trainer was almost unknown in those days, made no difference to Rose. From her earliest childhood, she was at home in the big cage with her father and his trained lions.

Monarch formed a deep affection for the little girl. He took the place that a dog or some other pet might take in the life of other children. Rosie played with him, tugged at his heavy mane and beard, and teased him in many little ways. Yet he took her teasing with a calm dignity, never for a moment losing his patience.

In those days, Captain Purchase's lion act was considered the best of its kind in all England. And the rare friendship between lion and child played no small part in its success.

As the years went by, Monarch began to grow old, and his master wanted to train a young lion to take his place. So it was that Sandy, a fine young lion, not yet in full mane, was bought and made part of the show. It became Monarch's business to help with the training and education of the younger animal.

From the first, Monarch made Sandy understand who was teacher and who was pupil. Sandy was quick and soon learned his part in the act. But he was jealous of his teacher, and waited only for the day when he might be strong enough to triumph over Monarch.

Old Monarch, slow on his feet, but still sure, was gradually losing his strength, and Sandy made the most of every chance to bully the old lion. He often snarled at him an invitation to fight.

Monarch had good sense and avoided a show-down. He knew by instinct the laws of nature. He knew that one day the young lion whom he had trained and with whom he had shared his cage and meat would rise up and try to conquer him. As much as possible, he kept clear of Sandy and paid no attention to his bullying. But things grew steadily worse.

Captain Purchase's lion act had been playing on the continent and had made a long trip home across Europe to London, where it was billed for a two weeks' engagement. There was a great crowd in the theater for the opening performance. A wave of excitement and cheers swept over the audience as a sharp whistle announced Captain Purchase and his two famous trained lions, Monarch and Sandy.

At a signal from the Captain both lions jumped to their pedestals and sat down. But all was not well. Sandy was in a very ugly mood. He hated to travel, and he was still in a bad temper from the long train and boat trip. He snarled at Monarch sitting a few feet away. His pedestal rocked and swayed. The Captain's whip cracked. Sandy snarled again, and lashed his tail from side to side.

The Captain blew his whistle and cracked his whip for the first cue. Both lions went into their act, but Sandy kept making trouble. Time and again, the Captain had to prompt him with the whip. But after each bit of the act the audience clapped and cheered.

Suddenly the big iron gate opened, and a girl came into the cage. It was Rose, Captain Purchase's little daughter.

As the gate shut quickly behind her, she went over to Monarch's pedestal, and, standing on her toes, she gave him a few affectionate slaps. Then she turned and saluted Sandy from where she stood. He sat there on his pedestal, his cold green cat-eyes peering at her from under his heavy brows, his head twisting from side to side, and his lips curled in a fierce snarl.

"Watch him, Rosie!" the Captain warned her. "Watch him. He's ugly tonight!"

With no thought of fear Rosie watched the show go on. The audience was amazed at the sight of a ten-year-old child in the big cage with the lions.

Before the last part of the act, the Captain stooped to pick up a new whip. For just a second, he faced the crowd with his back to the lions. In that second, Sandy jumped down off his pedestal and started walking toward the smiling Rose.

Without a sign of fear she stood there, backed against the bars, her hand stretched out, snapping her fingers, playfully coaxing the snarling beast.

"Come on, Sandy," she coaxed. "Come on, Sandy. Come on." And on he came.

The crowd shouted a warning and rose in horror. From his pedestal Monarch watched, his eyes shifting back and forth between Sandy and his master. In a flash the Captain turned. His whip cracked and his gun blazed.

Sandy stopped short and crouched in front of Rose. Then, lashing out with his huge right paw, he pinned her to the floor. Old Monarch roared and leaped from his pedestal to hurl himself at Sandy. The force of his attack was terrific. It took Sandy by surprise and threw him clear of the child. He tried to protect himself, but Monarch was too much for him. Sandy was conquered.

Looking around quickly, Monarch saw Rose safe on her feet and out of reach of Sandy. Cautiously, very, very cautiously, he loosed his hold on the other lion. Snarling, he backed slowly away until he was standing

beside the child. Rosie leaned up against Monarch, her fingers holding tight to his yellow mane. Still snarling, his lips curled, Monarch stood there watching Sandy's every move, waiting for him to attack again.

But Sandy was conquered once for all. And the cheers of the crowd told Monarch that once more he had been the star of the performance.

Later — perhaps some of you may have seen her — that same little girl became the famous Miss Rose Purchase, one of the greatest lion trainers the world has ever known.

Don Lang

179

ASHU AND THE WHIRLWIND

TALK OF A THIEF

ASHU was a daughter of the Jukons, once a mighty nation of warriors and priests in West Africa. She often thought with pride of her nation and of her tribe, but she was only thirteen years old, and sometimes other things seemed more important.

Just now Ashu stood in the little mud house that was her home, with a tiny mirror in her hand. She was trying to see in it the whole of her face at once. But when she saw one bright eye, the other disappeared from the little mirror, and when she saw her wide-lipped mouth with its flashing teeth, then her little black nose was out of the picture. She tried hardest of all to see an orange head-cloth, folded into a long flat piece and tied around her head like a turban. The ends were left flapping over one ear-ringed ear, and her curly hair stuck up through the center.

She made a little face at herself in the mirror. A cotton headcloth! Ashu, daughter of the Jukons, longed for silk. She had seen a certain silk handkerchief hanging in the booth of a trader in the market. She had cast longing eyes on it only yesterday, and the day before, and the day before that. It was a rich orange brocade, patterned with magenta — truly a wonderful headcloth. But it cost ten shillings, and she did not have ten shillings!

With a small sigh she slipped the mirror into a place between the grass roof and the wall of the mud house. Then, tightening her turban, she went out into the long slanting light of the hot afternoon.

Ashu's house, like all Jukon houses, had a walled-in compound, or yard, around which were grouped a number of small mud-walled and grass-roofed houses. The only way out from the compound to the street was through an entrance hut. Today everyone was away and the yard was empty. Chewing a kola nut, Ashu left the compound and wandered through the narrow streets. She was still trying to think of some way to get ten shillings.

Soon she came to the market-place, the center of the life of every African town. Men from the hills, clad only in breech cloths, were in sharp contrast to the chiefs of the district, who wore flowing white robes and huge spotless turbans. The smell of lemon oil mingled with the odors of dried fish and of freshly killed meat.

Ashu pressed through the market-day crowd, turning her back on the booth where the orange handkerchief hung. A storyteller was beating a drum in one corner of the market while he kept up an endless folk tale to amuse the crowd. Ashu joined the group but with only half an ear for the story he was telling.

Close to her stood two traders, talking quietly. Without meaning to listen, she heard their remarks above the drumming of the story teller.

". . . Amadu, the thief they call the Whirlwind, is in Wukari."

182

"The Whirlwind! What a curious name!" thought Ashu, and pressed closer that she might hear better above the beating of the story teller's drum.

The first trader, a tall man clad in a long blue robe, continued. "A large reward is offered for his capture, but the risk in taking him would be great. He has a charm that carries evil. All men know of it. His first wife made it for him, and Allah struck her with blindness. The charm is wicked beyond belief."

The shorter man gave a grunt of interest.

"This charm," went on the other, "he still has, and there is no charm to oppose it. I myself would like the reward, but I also value my life."

Just then the two men moved off, still talking.

Ashu noted that it was already quite dark, except for the full moon slowly rising through the trees. Very thoughtfully she turned her back on the market and wandered away. Who was this Amadu whom they called the Whirlwind?

Now she heard the sound of drumming in another part of the town, and hastened toward it. Some young people were grouped about two native drummers. They were dancing and shouting and clapping. Anyone who wished might join the dance.

Ashu tightened the cloth about her hips, gave an extra twist to her headcloth, and stepped into the dance. Slowly

183

the full moon rose. The red dust beat up from the hard-packed earth. The voices of singers rose and fell, and Ashu danced on and on.

It was nearing daylight and the moon was about to set, when the dancers began to drift away to their huts. Ashu, still not tired, was among the last to leave.

The town was never quite deserted at night, never wholly asleep. Ashu, having said her good nights in a high sweet voice, ran swiftly down the street. The moon was low now, and the street was dark. Ahead of her was a stranger, also moving quickly. She had noticed him some time before, as he stood watching the dancers from the shadow of a tree. He had a rapid walk, almost catlike, and the girl wondered who he might be. Her own feet made no sound on the dusty way.

Suddenly the stranger darted down the narrow opening into the small alley that led to Ashu's own house. As he turned, he gave a quick glance behind him. Ashu's figure melted into the black shadow of the high wall and he did not see her. She was close behind him now, and she saw him dodge quickly into the entrance of her father's compound. Suddenly remembering what she had heard earlier about a thief, Ashu also remembered that her father kept a heavy money box buried deep in the earth floor behind the entrance hut.

"Thou!" she called loudly, and rushed in after the man.

184

She saw the figure turn as she came up. She made a grab at him with one hand, but he slipped out of her grasp, and was gone through the entrance hut into the dark street.

One might as well try to catch a whirlwind. Whirlwind! This must be Amadu, the Whirlwind! Now she understood the reason for the name. The girl turned and went on into the compound, slowly, thoughtfully.

Danger in the Compound

On the following Friday, Gaddo, her father, who was a worker in leather, said that he planned to start for Ibi two days later, for a trading trip. Ashu decided to stay at home with the younger children. But the older women in the compound thought that they would go with Gaddo. The hairdresser in Ibi was known to be excellent and it was many weeks since they had had their hair dressed.

Thirty miles for a new hairdressing, then back again in a day or two — that was just a pleasure trip to an African native. On moonlight nights the roads were busy with an endless stream of travelers and traders. They came across the desert from Egypt, from the snowy mountains of the Cameroons, from French Senegal land, and from the jungles of the Gold Coast, always trading, always moving onward.

When the family had gone, Ashu went back to the

compound and made her plans. She was frightened, but excited and interested. If the man she had seen in her compound was the Whirlwind, he would come again. No doubt he would hear of the family trip, and take advantage of it.

Cleverly, she managed that evening to coax some girls who had started dancing in the next street to come into the compound of her own house. The dance lasted very late. When the drummers finally left, some of the girls stayed on, eating mangoes, telling stories, and chattering till daylight. No thief would enter while they were there.

It was late the next morning when Ashu started for market, with a plan in the back of her head.

When she reached the market-place, she joined a group of men who sat talking in the shade of one of the small market booths. Among them was her uncle Ablus, who was her father's brother and a policeman of Wukari. As the morning was hot, he had taken off his heavy red turban. It lay behind him as he talked, along with his red cotton shoulder band and the handcuffs that he usually carried by his side. These handcuffs Ashu needed for her plan.

She crept into the shade and sat down next to Ablus. He gave her a smile, patted her hand, and went on talking with the other men. Half an hour later, when Ashu got up to leave, he did not even look up. So he did not know that the handcuffs lay in the bottom of her calabash, beneath some corn she was carrying.

That evening, Ashu did not feel nearly so brave as she had felt earlier in the day. It was all very well to plan in broad daylight to catch a thief, and to work all day to set a trap for him. It was another thing to wait at night with pounding heart, in the dark stillness of the little entrance hut, to carry out the plan. Her mouth was dry. Her knees were shaking. She lay down on the mat which she had dragged from her own hut and pretended to be asleep.

Before long she heard a slight sound. She peered out from beneath her arm. Surely a shadow had crossed the moonlight in the doorway.

She was right. A shadow had. Someone was beginning to dig, softly, in the place just inside the compound wall. Ashu, her heart starting to pound all over again, gave a little sigh, intending it should be heard.

It had hardly been uttered before the Whirlwind, living up to his name, was beside her. He laid a heavy hand on her mouth.

"Who is that?" he asked sharply. Then, realizing that it was only a girl, he lifted his hand that she might reply, but he still kept a rough hold on her shoulder.

"I am Ashu, the daughter of Gaddo!" she answered, and struggled to sit up.

There was silence for a moment. Then a voice demanded, "Are you alone in the compound?"

"There is no one else here but the small children," said Ashu.

The Whirlwind's hand slipped from her shoulder and Ashu's courage began to come back. Perhaps her plan might work, after all.

"Come!" ordered the thief in a whisper. "Show me the place where the silver is hidden."

His hand pulled her toward the wall, where, indeed, the money was buried. He let go her wrist and pressed a sharp knife against her side.

"Dig!" he ordered in a low voice. "You know where. Let the work be swift."

188

Ashu's hands found the small jungle knife with which the Whirlwind had started to dig up the earth. Pretending to work swiftly, Ashu nevertheless took her time. Meanwhile, the knife pressed unpleasantly against her side, and pressed even closer when the sound of voices came from the street.

Ashu pushed at the loose earth with swift brown hands, and the Whirlwind, eager and quick, soon laid down the knife to help.

Ashu dug deeper and deeper. The moon rose higher and higher. At last she felt the touch of cold iron, down an arm's length into the cool earth.

"Here is what you seek," she said.

"Where?" said the Whirlwind. "Show me!"

His hand was on her wrist and she guided it down, down in the darkness. There was a little exclamation from him as he felt the iron.

"You'll need both hands," she suggested. "It's all in an iron box, one of the white man's boxes. It is very heavy."

Her arm was still in the hole, while he was stretched out beside her, to reach both hands after hers. Roughly he pushed her aside.

"Let me be. I will do it alone," he said.

But Ashu's hand was still guiding his fingers. Suddenly there was the sound of a metal click. Ashu sprang up.

Amadu, the Whirlwind, lay face down, his arms in the hole. His wrists were held tightly by the handcuffs Ashu had that afternoon fastened to the handle of the heavy iron box. Her plan had worked!

Hugging herself with delight, the girl ran through the streets in the moonlight, straight to the house of her uncle, the policeman. She went to tell him where he could find his handcuffs.

It was a week later. Ashu peered into her little mirror admiringly. On top of her curly hair was a splendid silk handkerchief of flaming orange, patterned with magenta. She had received a good reward for the capture of the Whirlwind in the very act of robbing her father. She patted the handkerchief happily.

Erick Berry

190

MARATHON

King Darius comes from the tiger-hunt
And sits on a golden chair;
They bring him sherbets in cool gold cups,
His roses drench the air.

Before the might of Persia's lord
The knees of his slaves are bowed;
King Darius shines like the sun at noon,
But his scowl is dark as a cloud.

His tribute flows from east and west.
What more is it Persia seeks?
King Darius growls in his curled black beard,
"I do not like these Greeks!"

He has sent his envoys across the sea
To the poor little city-state.
"Let them know that I am king of kings,
And Persia forever great."

Said he, "Let them give my messengers
A little water and earth,
In token that they submit to us,
And know what our power is worth."

The Greeks, they heard the Persian's word,
But the freemen's answer was rough;
They threw the messengers into a well
Where was water and earth enough.

Darius summons ships and men;
Their spears shine in the sun;
He has sent his fleet across the sea
That the Greeks may be undone.

But where the ships of Darius sailed,
Old Neptune turned around
And shook his shoulders and roared and stormed,
Till the Persians all were drowned.

King Darius' scowl was dark as a cloud,
He growled in his curled black beard.
He bided his time, he builded his ships,
That the Greeks might be afeared.

Forth went the Persian host once more;
Their spears were many as rain.
They sailed, they sailed, they sailed, and sailed
Till they came nigh Marathon plain.

Upon the hills round Marathon
The free Athenians stood,
Ten thousand strong, all bound to save
Greek freedom with their blood.

Pheidippides, the runner, sped
To beg for Spartan aid;
Then home he ran to tell the word.
"No help," the Spartans said.

Then forth again to join the troops
Pheidippides ran on,
No man of Athens but must fight
The fight of Marathon.

The Persian arrows flew like hail,
Like hail, the Persian spears;
The folk of Athens watched by night;
Their eyes were bright with tears.

The folk of Athens watched till dawn,
And then a dust-cloud showed,
A runner with his news it was
Upon the northern road.

Pheidippides, the runner, flew,
His throat on fire with drouth,
With aching lungs, with bleeding feet,
And the dust it burned his mouth.

He scarce had breath to tell the news;
He spoke three words, and none
But shook with joy to hear him gasp
The wonder, "We have won!"

Let Darius sit on a golden chair
And drink from a cup of gold,
But never the dazzling tale will fade
That the dying runner told.

The pomp of Persia has withered away,
Greek glory lingers on,
And still free men rejoice when they
Remember Marathon.

Babette Deutsch

GHOST OF THE LAGOON

THE KING'S REWARD

THE island of Bora Bora, where Mako lived, is far away in the south Pacific. It is not a large island — you can paddle around it in a single day — but the main body of it rises straight out of the sea, very high into the air, like a castle. Waterfalls trail down the faces of the cliffs. As you look upward, you see wild goats leaping from crag to crag.

Mako had been born on the very edge of the sea, and most of his waking hours were spent in the waters of the lagoon, which was nearly enclosed by the two out-stretched arms of the island. He was very clever with his hands; he had made a harpoon that was as straight as an arrow, and tipped with five, pointed, iron spears. He had made a canoe, hollowing it out of a tree. It wasn't a very big canoe — only a little longer than his own height. It had an outrigger, a sort of balancing pole, fastened to one side to keep the boat from tipping over. The canoe was just large enough to hold Mako and his little dog, Afa. They were great companions, these two.

One evening Mako lay stretched at full length on the pandanus mats, listening to Grandfather's voice. Overhead, stars shone in the dark sky. From far off came the thunder of the surf on the reef.

The old man was speaking of Tupa, the ghost of the lagoon. Ever since the boy could remember, he had heard tales of this terrible monster. Frightened fishermen, returning from the reef at midnight, spoke of the ghost. Over the evening fires, old men told endless tales about the monster.

Tupa seemed to think the lagoon of Bora Bora belonged to him. The natives left presents of food for him out on the reef: a dead goat, a chicken, or a pig. The presents always disappeared mysteriously, but everyone felt sure that it was Tupa who carried them away. Still, in spite of all this food, the nets of the fishermen were torn during the night, the fish stolen. What an appetite Tupa seemed to have!

Not many people had ever seen the ghost of the lagoon. Grandfather was one of the few who had.

"What does he really look like, Grandfather?" the boy asked, for the hundredth time.

The old man shook his head solemnly. The light from the cook-fire glistened on his white hair. "Tupa lives in the great caves of the reef. He is longer than this house. There is a sail on his back, not large, but terrible to see, for it burns with a white fire. Once, when I was fishing beyond the reef at night, I saw him come up right under another canoe — "

"What happened then?" Mako asked. He half rose on one elbow. This was a story he had not heard before.

The old man's voice dropped to a whisper. "Tupa dragged the canoe right under the water — and the water boiled with white flame. The three fishermen in it were never seen again. Fine swimmers they were, too."

Grandfather shook his head. "It is bad fortune even to speak of Tupa. There is evil in his very name."

"But King Opu Nui has offered a reward for his capture," the boy pointed out.

"Thirty acres of fine coconut land, and a sailing canoe as well," said the old man. "But who ever heard of laying hands on a ghost?"

Mako's eyes glistened. "Thirty acres of land and a sailing canoe. How I should love to win that reward!"

Grandfather nodded, but Mako's mother scolded her son for such foolish talk. "Be quiet now, son, and go to sleep. Grandfather has told you that it is bad fortune to speak of Tupa. Alas, how well we have learned that lesson! Your father — " She stopped herself.

"What of my father?" the boy asked quickly. And now he sat up straight on the mats.

"Tell him, Grandfather," his mother whispered.

The old man cleared his throat and poked at the fire. A little shower of sparks whirled up into the darkness.

"Your father," he explained gently, "was one of the three fishermen in the canoe that Tupa destroyed." His words fell upon the air like stones dropped into a deep well.

Mako shivered. He brushed back the hair from his damp forehead. Then he squared his shoulders and cried fiercely, "I shall slay Tupa and win the King's reward!" He rose to his knees, his slim body tense, his eyes flashing in the firelight.

"Hush!" his mother said. "Go to sleep now. Enough of such foolish talk. Would you bring trouble upon us all?"

Mako lay down again upon the mats. He rolled over on his side and closed his eyes, but sleep was long in coming.

The palm trees whispered above the dark lagoon, and far out on the reef the sea thundered.

A Trip to the Reef

The boy was slow to wake up the next morning. The ghost of Tupa had played through his dreams, making him restless. And so it was almost noon before Mako sat up on the mats and stretched himself. He called Afa, and the boy and his dog ran down to the lagoon for their morning swim.

When they returned to the house, wide awake and hungry, Mako's mother had food ready and waiting.

"These are the last of our bananas," she told him. "I wish you would paddle out to the reef this afternoon and bring back a new bunch."

The boy agreed eagerly. Nothing pleased him more than such an errand, which would take him to a little island on the outer reef, half a mile from shore. It was one of Mako's favorite playgrounds, and there bananas and oranges grew in great plenty.

"Come, Afa," he called, gulping the last mouthful. "We're going on an expedition." He picked up his long-bladed knife and seized his spear. A minute later, he dashed across the white sand, where his canoe was drawn up beyond the water's reach.

Afa barked at his heels. He was all white except for a black spot over each eye. Wherever Mako went, there went Afa also. Now the little dog leaped into the bow of the canoe, his tail wagging with delight. The boy pushed the canoe into the water and climbed aboard. Then, picking up his paddle, he thrust it into the water. The canoe shot ahead. Its sharp bow cut through the green water of the lagoon like a knife through cheese. And so clear was the water that Mako could see the coral gardens, forty feet below him, growing in the sand. The shadow of the canoe moved over them.

A school of fish swept by like silver arrows. He saw scarlet rock cod with ruby eyes and the head of a conger eel peering out from a cavern in the coral. The boy thought suddenly of Tupa, ghost of the lagoon. On such a bright day it was hard to believe in ghosts of any sort. The fierce sunlight drove away all thought of them. Perhaps ghosts were only old men's stories, anyway!

Mako's eyes came to rest upon his spear — the spear that he had made with his own hands — the spear that was as straight and true as an arrow. He remembered his

200

vow of the night before. Could a ghost be killed with a spear? Some night, when all the village was sleeping, Mako swore to himself that he would find out! He would paddle out to the reef and challenge Tupa! Perhaps tonight. Why not? He caught his breath at the thought. A shiver ran down his back. His hands were tense on the paddle.

As the canoe drew away from shore, the boy saw the coral reef that, above all others, had always interested him. It was of white coral — a long slim shape that rose slightly above the surface of the water. It looked very much like a shark. There was a ridge on the back that the boy could pretend was a dorsal fin, while up near one end were two dark holes that looked like eyes! Times without number the boy had practiced spearing this make-believe shark, aiming always for the eyes, the most vulnerable spot. So true and straight had his aim become that the spear would pass right into the eyeholes without even touching the sides of the coral. Mako had nicknamed the coral reef "Tupa."

This morning, as he paddled past it, he shook his fist and called, "Ho, Mister Tupa! Just wait till I get my bananas. When I come back I'll make short work of you!"

Afa followed his master's words with a sharp bark. He knew Mako was excited about something.

The bow of the canoe touched the sand of the little island where the bananas grew. Afa leaped ashore and ran barking into the jungle, now on this trail, now on that.

Clouds of sea birds whirled from their nests into the air with angry cries.

Mako climbed into the shallow water, waded ashore, and pulled his canoe up on the beach. Then, picking up his banana knife, he followed Afa. In the jungle the light was so dense and green that the boy felt as if he were moving under water. Ferns grew higher than his head. The branches of the trees formed a green roof over him. A flock of parakeets fled on swift wings. Somewhere a wild pig crashed through the undergrowth while Afa dashed away in pursuit. Mako paused anxiously. Armed only with his banana knife, he had no desire to meet the wild pig. The pig, it seemed, had no desire to meet him, either.

Then, ahead of him, the boy saw the broad green blades

of a banana tree. A bunch of bananas, golden ripe, was growing out of the top.

At the foot of the tree he made a nest of soft leaves for the bunch to fall upon. In this way the fruit wouldn't be crushed. Then with a swift slash of his blade he cut the stem. The bananas fell to the earth with a dull thud. He found two more bunches.

Then he thought, "I might as well get some oranges while I'm here. Those little rusty ones are sweeter than any that grow on Bora Bora."

So he set about making a net out of palm leaves to carry the oranges. As he worked, his swift fingers moving in and out among the strong green leaves, he could hear Afa's excited barks off in the jungle. That was just like Afa, always barking at something: a bird, a fish, a wild pig. He never caught anything, either. Still, no boy ever had a finer companion.

The palm net took longer to make than Mako had realized. By the time it was finished and filled with oranges, the jungle was dark and gloomy. Night comes quickly and without warning in the islands of the tropics.

Mako carried the fruit down to the shore and loaded it into the canoe. Then he whistled to Afa. The dog came bounding out of the bush, wagging his tail.

"Hurry!" Mako scolded. "We won't be home before the dark comes."

The little dog leaped into the bow of the canoe and Mako came aboard. Night seemed to rise up from the surface of the water and swallow them. On the distant shore of Bora Bora, cook-fires were being lighted. The first star twinkled just over the dark mountains. Mako dug his paddle into the water and the canoe leaped ahead.

The dark water was alive with phosphorus. The bow of the canoe seemed to cut through a pale liquid fire. Each dip of the paddle trailed streamers of light. As the canoe approached the coral reef, the boy called, "Ho, Tupa! It's too late tonight to teach you your lesson. But I'll come back tomorrow." The coral shark glistened in the darkness.

And then, suddenly, Mako's breath caught in his throat. His hands felt weak. Just beyond the fin of the coral Tupa, there was another fin — a huge one. It had never been there before. And — could he believe his eyes? It was moving!

The boy stopped paddling. He dashed his hand across his eyes. Afa began to bark furiously. The great white fin, shaped like a small sail, glowed with phosphorescent light. Then Mako knew. Here was Tupa — the real Tupa — ghost of the lagoon!

204

His knees felt weak. He tried to cry out, but his voice died in his throat. The great shark was circling slowly around the canoe. With each circle, it moved closer and closer. Now the boy could see the phosphorescent glow of the great shark's sides. As it moved in closer, he saw the yellow eyes, the gill-slits in its throat.

Afa leaped from one side of the canoe to the other. In sudden anger Mako leaned forward to grab the dog and shake him soundly. Afa wriggled out of his grasp, as Mako tried to catch him, and the shift in weight tipped the canoe on one side. The outrigger rose from the water. In another second they would be overboard. The boy threw his weight over quickly to balance the canoe, but with a loud splash Afa fell over into the dark water.

Mako stared after him in dismay. The little dog, instead of swimming back to the canoe, had headed for the distant shore. And there was the great white shark — very near.

"Afa! Afa! Come back! Come quickly!" Mako shouted.

The little dog turned back toward the canoe. He was swimming with all his strength. Mako leaned forward. Could Afa make it? Swiftly the boy seized his spear. Bracing himself, he stood upright. There was no weakness in him now. His dog, his companion, was in danger of instant death.

Afa was swimming desperately to reach the canoe. The white shark had paused in his circling to gather speed for the attack. Mako raised his arm, took aim. In that instant the shark charged. Mako's arm flashed forward. All his strength was behind that thrust. The spear drove straight and true, right into the great shark's eye. Mad with pain and rage, Tupa whipped about, lashing the water in fury. The canoe rocked back and forth. Mako struggled to keep his balance as he drew back the spear by the cord fastened to his wrist.

He bent over to seize Afa and drag him aboard. Then he stood up, not a moment too soon. Once again the

shark charged. Once again Mako threw his spear, this time at the other eye. The spear found its mark. Blinded and weak from loss of blood, Tupa rolled to the surface, turned slightly on his side. Was he dead?

Mako knew how clever sharks could be, and he was taking no chances. Scarcely daring to breathe, he paddled toward the still body. He saw the faintest motion of the great tail. The shark was still alive. The boy knew that one flip of that tail could overturn the canoe and send him and Afa into the water, where Tupa could destroy them.

Swiftly, yet calmly, Mako stood upright and braced himself firmly. Then, murmuring a silent prayer to the Shark God, he threw his spear for the last time. Downward, swift as sound, the spear plunged into a white shoulder.

Peering over the side of the canoe, Mako could see the great fish turn over far below the surface. Then slowly, slowly, the great shark rose to the surface of the lagoon. There he floated, half on one side.

Tupa was dead.

Mako flung back his head and shouted for joy. Hitching a strong line about the shark's tail, the boy began to paddle toward the shore of Bora Bora. The dorsal fin, burning with the white fire of phosphorus, trailed after the canoe.

Men were running down the beaches of Bora Bora, shouting as they leaped into their canoes and put out across the lagoon. Their cries reached the boy's ears across the water.

"It is Tupa — ghost of the lagoon," he heard them shout. "Mako has killed him!"

That night, as the tired boy lay on the pandanus mats listening to the distant thunder of the sea, he heard Grandfather singing a new song. It was the song which would be sung the next day at the feast which King Opu Nui would give in Mako's honor. The boy saw his mother bending over the cook-fire. The stars leaned close, winking like friendly eyes. Grandfather's voice reached him now from a great distance, "Thirty acres of land and a sailing canoe. . . ."

Armstrong Sperry

MIGHTY MAGIC

THE RIDE-BY-NIGHTS

UP ON their brooms the Witches stream,
Crooked and black in the crescent's gleam;
One foot high, and one foot low,
Bearded, cloaked, and cowled, they go.
'Neath Charlie's Wain they twitter and tweet,
And away they swarm 'neath the Dragon's feet.
With a whoop and a flutter they swing and sway,

And surge pell-mell down the Milky Way.
Betwixt the legs of the glittering Chair
They hover and squeak in the empty air.
Then round they swoop past the glimmering Lion
To where Sirius barks behind huge Orion;
Up, then, and over to wheel amain,
Under the silver, and home again.

Walter de la Mare

MIGHTY MIKKO

A POOR WOODSMAN

THERE was once an old woodsman and his wife who had an only son named Mikko. As the mother lay dying, the young man wept bitterly.

"When you are gone, my dear mother," he said, "there will be no one left to think of me."

The poor woman comforted him as best she could and said to him, "You will still have your father."

Shortly after the woman's death, the old man, too, was taken ill.

"Now, indeed, I shall be sad and lonely," Mikko thought, as he sat beside his father's bedside and saw him grow weaker and weaker.

"My boy," the old man said just before he died, "I have nothing to leave you but the three snares with which I have caught wild animals these many years. Those snares now belong to you. When I am dead, go into the woods, and if you find a wild creature caught in any of them, free it gently and bring it home alive."

After his father's death, Mikko remembered the snares and went out to the woods to look at them. The first was empty and also the second, but in the third he found a little red Fox. He carefully loosened the noose that was caught around one of the Fox's feet, and then carried the little creature home in his arms. He shared his supper with it, and when he lay down to sleep, the Fox curled up at his feet. They lived together some time until they became close friends.

"Mikko," said the Fox one day, "why are you so sad?"

"Because I'm lonely."

"Pooh!" said the Fox. "That's no way for a young man to talk! You ought to get married. Then you wouldn't feel lonely."

"Married!" Mikko repeated. "How can I get married? I can't marry a poor girl because I'm too poor myself and a rich girl wouldn't marry me."

"Nonsense!" said the Fox. "You're a fine well-set-up young man and you're kind and gentle. What more could a princess ask?"

Mikko laughed to think of a princess wanting him for a husband.

"I mean what I say!" the Fox insisted. "Take our own Princess now. What would you think of marrying her?"

Mikko laughed louder than before. "I have heard," he said, "that she is the most beautiful princess in the world. Any man would be happy to marry her."

"Very well," the Fox said. "If you feel that way about her, then I'll arrange the wedding for you."

With that the little Fox went trotting off to the royal castle and gained audience with the King.

"My master sends you greetings," the Fox said, "and he begs you to lend him your bushel measure."

"My bushel measure!" the King repeated in surprise. "Who is your master and why does he want my bushel measure?"

"Ssh!" the Fox whispered, as though he didn't want the courtiers to hear what he was saying. Then, slipping up quite close to the King, he murmured in his ear, "Surely you have heard of Mikko, haven't you? — Mighty Mikko as he's called?"

The King had never heard of any Mikko who was known as Mighty Mikko, but, thinking that perhaps he should have heard of him, he shook his head and murmured, "H'm! Mikko! Mighty Mikko! Oh, to be sure! Yes, yes, of course!"

"My master is about to start off on a journey and he needs a bushel measure for a very special reason."

"I understand! I understand!" the King said, although he didn't understand at all, and he gave orders that the bushel measure which they used in the storeroom of the castle be brought in and given to the Fox.

The Fox carried off the measure and hid it in the woods. Then he hurried about to all sorts of little out-of-the-way places where people had hidden their savings, and he dug up a gold piece here and a silver piece there until he had a handful. Then he went back to the woods and stuck the coins in the cracks of the measure. The next day he returned to the King.

"My master, Mighty Mikko," he said, "sends you thanks, O King, for the use of your bushel measure."

The King held out his hand. When the Fox gave him the measure he peeped inside to see if by chance it held any sign of what had recently been measured. His eye, of course, at once caught the gleam of the gold and silver coins lodged in the cracks.

"Ah!" he said, thinking Mikko must be a very mighty lord indeed to be so careless of his wealth. "I should like to meet your master. Won't you and he come and visit me?"

This was what the Fox wanted the King to say but he pretended to hesitate.

"I thank your Majesty for the kind invitation," he said, "but I fear my master can't accept it just now. He wants to get married soon, and we are about to start off on a long journey to visit a number of foreign princesses."

This made the King all the more anxious to have Mikko visit him at once, for he thought that if Mikko should see his daughter before he saw those foreign princesses he might fall in love with her and marry her. So he said to the Fox, "My dear fellow, you must persuade your master to make me a visit before he starts out on his travels. You will, won't you?"

The Fox looked this way and that as if he were too embarrassed to speak.

"Your Majesty," he said at last, "the truth is you are not rich enough to entertain my master, and your castle isn't big enough to house the great number of servants who always attend him."

The King, who by this time was frantic to see Mikko, lost his head completely.

"My dear Fox," he said, "I'll give you anything in the world if you persuade your master to visit me at once. Couldn't you suggest to him to travel with a few servants this time?"

The Fox shook his head.

"No. His rule is either to travel as a prince should or to go on foot, disguised as a poor woodsman."

"Couldn't you persuade him to come to me disguised as a poor woodsman?" the King begged. "Once he was here, I could place gorgeous clothes at his service."

Still the Fox shook his head.

"I fear your Majesty doesn't own the kind of clothes my master usually wears."

"I have some very good clothes," the King said. "Come along this minute and we'll go through them and I'm sure you'll find some that your master would wear."

So they went to a room with hundreds and hundreds of hooks upon which were hung hundreds of coats and breeches and embroidered shirts. The King ordered his servants to take down the suits, one by one, and place them before the Fox.

They began with the plainer clothes.

"Good enough for most people," the Fox said, "but not for my master."

Then they took down suits of a better grade.

"I'm afraid you're going to all this trouble for nothing," the Fox said. "Frankly now, don't you realize that my master couldn't possibly put on any of these things?"

The King, who had hoped to keep for his own use his most gorgeous clothes of all, now ordered these to be shown.

The Fox looked at them sideways, sniffed them, and at last said, "Well, perhaps my master would consent to wear these for a few days. They are not what he usually wears but I will say this for him — he is not proud."

The King was overjoyed.

"Very well, my dear Fox, I'll have the guest rooms made ready for your master's visit, and I'll have all these, my finest clothes, laid out for him. You won't disappoint me, will you?"

"I'll do my best," the Fox promised.

With that he bade the King a polite good day and ran home to Mikko.

The Clever Fox

The next day, as the Princess was peeping out of an upper window of the castle, she saw a young woodsman approaching, accompanied by a Fox. The youth was fine-looking, and the Princess, who knew from the presence of the Fox that he must be Mikko, gave a long sigh and said to her serving maid, "I think I could fall in love with that young man if he really were only a woodsman!"

Later, when she saw him dressed in her father's finest clothes — which looked so well on Mikko that no one even recognized them as the King's — she lost her heart completely.

All the Court was equally delighted with Mikko. The ladies were loud in praise of his modest manners, his fine figure, and the gorgeousness of his clothes. The old graybeard Councilors, nodding their heads in approval, said to one another, "In spite of his great wealth, see how politely he listens to us when we talk!"

The next day the Fox went secretly to the King, and said, "My master is a man of few words and quick judgment. He bids me tell you that your daughter, the Princess, pleases him greatly and that, with your approval, he would like to marry her."

The King was greatly excited and began, "My dear Fox — "

But the Fox interrupted him to say, "Think the matter over carefully and give me your decision tomorrow."

So the King consulted with the Princess and with his Councilors, and in a short time the marriage was arranged and the wedding ceremony really performed.

"Didn't I tell you?" the Fox said, when he and Mikko were alone after the wedding.

"Yes," Mikko admitted, "you did promise that I should marry the Princess. But tell me, now that I am married, what am I to do? I can't live on here forever with my wife."

"Put your mind at rest," the Fox said. "I've thought of everything. Just do as I tell you and you'll have nothing to regret. Tonight, say to the King, 'It is now only fitting that you should visit me and see for yourself the sort of castle over which your daughter is to be mistress!' "

When Mikko said this to the King, the King was overjoyed, for now that the marriage had really taken place, he was wondering whether he hadn't perhaps been a little hasty. Mikko's words reassured him and he eagerly accepted the invitation.

On the morrow the Fox said to Mikko, "Now I'll run on ahead and get things ready for you."

"But where are you going?" Mikko said, frightened at the thought of being deserted by his little friend.

The Fox drew Mikko aside and whispered softly, "A few days' march from here there is a very gorgeous castle belonging to a wicked old dragon who is known as the Worm. I think the Worm's castle would just about suit you."

"I'm sure it would," Mikko agreed. "But how are we to get it away from the Worm?"

"Trust me," the Fox said. "All you need do is this: lead the King and his courtiers along the main highway until by noon tomorrow you reach a crossroads. Turn there to the left and go straight on until you see the tower of the Worm's castle. If you meet any men by the way, shepherds or the like, ask them whose men they are and show no surprise at their answer. So now, dear master, good-by until we meet again at your beautiful castle."

The little Fox trotted off quickly and Mikko and the Princess and the King, attended by the whole Court, followed more slowly.

The little Fox, when he had left the main highway at the crossroads, soon met ten woodsmen with axes over

their shoulders. They were all dressed in blue smocks of the same cut.

"Good day," the Fox said politely. "Whose men are you?"

"Our master is known as the Worm," the woodsmen told him.

"My poor, poor lads!" the Fox said, shaking his head sadly.

"What's the matter?" the woodsmen asked.

For a few moments the Fox pretended to be too over-come to speak. Then he said, "My poor lads, don't you know that the King is coming with a great force to destroy the Worm and all his people?"

The woodsmen were simple fellows and this news made them tremble in fear.

"Is there no way for us to escape?" they asked.

The Fox put his paw to his head and thought hard.

"Well," he said at last, "there is one way you might escape and that is by telling everyone who asks you that you are the Mighty Mikko's men. But if you value your lives, never again say that your master is the Worm."

"We are Mighty Mikko's men!" the woodsmen at once began repeating over and over. "We are Mighty Mikko's men!"

A little farther on the road, the Fox met twenty grooms, dressed in similar blue smocks, who were tending a hundred beautiful horses. The Fox talked to the twenty grooms as he had talked to the woodsmen, and before he left them they, too, were shouting, "We are Mighty Mikko's men!"

Next, the Fox came to a huge flock of a thousand sheep, tended by thirty shepherds all dressed in the Worm's blue smocks. He stopped and talked to them until he had them roaring out, "We are Mighty Mikko's men!"

Then the Fox trotted on until he reached the castle of the Worm. He found the Worm himself inside, half asleep. He was a huge dragon and had been a great warrior in his day. In fact, his castle and his lands and his servants and his possessions had all been won in battle. But now for many years no one had cared to fight him and he had grown fat and lazy.

"Good day," the Fox said, pretending to be very breathless and frightened. "You're the Worm, aren't you?"

"Yes," the dragon boasted, "I am the great Worm!"

The Fox pretended to grow more excited.

"My poor fellow, I am sorry for you! But, of course, none of us can expect to live forever. Well, I must hurry along. I just thought I would stop and say good-by."

Made uneasy by the Fox's words, the Worm cried out, "Wait just a minute! What's the matter?"

The Fox was already at the door, but at the Worm's words he paused and said over his shoulder, "Why, my poor fellow, you surely know that the King with a great force is coming to destroy you and all your people?"

"What!" the Worm gasped, turning green with fright. He knew he was fat and helpless and could never again fight as in the years gone by.

"Don't go just yet!" he begged the Fox. "When is the King coming?"

"He's on the way now. That's why I must go."

"My dear Fox, stay just a moment and I'll reward you richly. Help me to hide so that the King won't find me. What about the shed where the linen is stored? I could crawl under the linen and then if you locked the door from the outside, the King could never find me."

"Very well," the Fox agreed, "but we must hurry!"

So they ran outside to the shed where the linen was kept, and the Worm hid himself under the linen. The Fox locked the door, then set fire to the shed, and soon there was nothing left of that wicked old dragon, the Worm, but a handful of ashes.

The Fox now called together the dragon's household and won them over to Mikko as he had the woodsmen and the grooms and the shepherds.

Meanwhile, the King and his party were slowly covering the ground over which the Fox had sped so quickly. When they came to the ten woodsmen in blue smocks, the King said, "I wonder whose woodsmen those are."

One of his courtiers asked the woodsmen, and the ten of them shouted out at the top of their voices, "We are Mighty Mikko's men!"

Mikko said nothing and the King and all the Court thought Mikko was being very modest.

A little farther on, they met the twenty grooms with their hundred prancing horses. When the grooms were questioned, they answered with a shout, "We are Mighty Mikko's men!"

"The Fox certainly spoke the truth," the King thought to himself, "when he told me of Mikko's riches."

A little later the thirty shepherds, when they were questioned, made answer in a chorus that was deafening to hear, "We are Mighty Mikko's men!"

The sight of the thousand sheep that belonged to his son-in-law made the King feel poor in comparison, and the courtiers whispered among themselves, "For all his simple manner, Mighty Mikko must be a richer, more powerful lord than the King himself. In fact it is only a very great lord indeed who could be so simple."

At last they reached the castle which had belonged to the Worm. The Fox came out to welcome the King's party, and behind him in two rows stood all the household servants dressed in blue smocks. These, at a signal from the Fox shouted, "We are Mighty Mikko's men!"

Then Mikko, in the same simple manner that he would have used in his father's poor little hut in the woods, made the King and his followers welcome. They all entered the castle, where they found a great feast waiting.

The King stayed several days. The more he saw of Mikko the better pleased he was with his son-in-law.

When he was leaving he said to Mikko, "Your castle is so much grander than mine that I hesitate to ask you back for a visit."

But Mikko told the King, "My dear father-in-law, when first I entered your castle I thought it was the most beautiful castle in the world."

The King was pleased and the courtiers whispered among themselves, "How noble of him to say that when he knows very well how much grander his own castle is!"

When the King and his followers were safely gone, the little red Fox came to Mikko and said, "Now, my master, you have no reason to feel sad and lonely. You are lord of the most beautiful castle in the world and you have for a wife a sweet and lovely princess. You have no longer any need of me, so I am going to bid you good-by."

Mikko thanked the little Fox for all he had done and the little Fox trotted off to the woods.

So you see that Mikko's poor old father, although he had no wealth to leave his son, was really the cause of all Mikko's good fortune, for it was he who told Mikko in the first place to carry home alive anything he might find caught in the snares.

Parker Fillmore

THE TERRIBLE STRANGER

FERGUS, THE BATTLE-WINNER

NIGHT came down cold and dark over the white ground. The chariot tracks were deep as a man's arm. The winter wind swept across the plain and howled around the Royal House.

All was light and warmth inside. The glow of blazing logs reddened the walls and glimmered on the silver and bronze ornaments. The smell of burning wood was in

the air, and the voices of
poets and of harps drifted
from the king's chamber.
The huge Warrior's Hall was
a happy place this night,
where a group of Knights of
the Red Branch of Ulster had
drawn close to the fire.

It had been a good year,
this long-ago year that was
coming to an end. They
talked of their victories, and
of the great herds and rich
crops of Ulster. And they
didn't fail to credit to themselves all the power and splendor of the kingdom.

Suddenly the noise of their voices ceased. And it wasn't
the music that stopped them, nor the door bursting open
with a great slam, nor even the big whirl of snow that blew
in at them and kept whirling around the room.

No, it was the terrible figure they saw standing there
that put the silence on them — the figure of a tall man,
awkward and ugly, with stooped shoulders and hungry
yellow eyes and a scraggly beard. He had an old cowhide
wrapped about him, and in his hand he held a great ax.

Fergus, a big knight with reddish-yellow hair, turned and faced the stranger. "What do you want?" he asked.

The stranger frowned at him. "I am looking for a man," he answered, and his voice seemed to rumble like thunder from far down in the cowhide.

MacRoi, another knight of the Red Branch, gave a twist to his red beard. "A man shouldn't be hard to find," he said, "not here." And he looked down at himself proudly. "Who are you?"

"Hoth," answered the stranger.

"H'm! Well, what sort of man is it you want?"

Hoth pulled out a hair from his beard and dropped it on the gleaming edge of his ax, where it fell in two pieces.

"The man I want," he said, "is the kind that is hard to find. He is hard to find in good times, and he is hard to find in bad times. But I don't know that there is a better when he is found. And that is the kind who will keep an agreement."

"You would have to go out of this kingdom to find one that wouldn't," growled Fergus.

"An Ulsterman keeps his word," said MacRoi. "I remember well the time — "

"It is expected of him," Fergus interrupted.

Hoth looked around the hall and his eyes seemed to see into all the dark corners, even up into the black beams overhead.

"That is all I want," he said, "just the keeping of an agreement."

"What a pity Cuchulain is not here," said Red MacRoi. "He is a great lad for keeping his word. There are not many like Cuchulain and me. What sort of agreement is it you want kept?"

"This," replied Hoth. "I am looking for a man who will keep this agreement with me: he is to cut off my head tonight, and I am to cut off his head tomorrow night."

MacRoi made a neat little curl on the end of his beard. "You give him all the advantage," he remarked.

"Advantage or no advantage," Hoth growled, "that is the agreement: he to cut off my head tonight, I to cut off his head tomorrow night."

"Cuchulain would like that," said MacRoi, "anything that had cutting off heads in it. He would keep his agreement, too, Cuchulain would, if he were here. Not but it is a queer enough one."

"It is the one I want," Hoth mumbled. "Where is this Cuchulain?"

Fergus got up. "Cuchulain is away now, but he is not the only man that keeps his word," said he, and he flung off his blue cloak. "Neither Cuchulain nor any man is the equal of myself. I am the Winner of Battles. Is there a single warrior in all Ireland that ever got the better of me? Is there one that can compare with me? Are there any ten men that are half as good as I am? Are there? You say you want me to cut off your head?"

"Mine, tonight," Hoth said solemnly. "Yours, tomorrow night. That is the agreement, if you will make it."

"Where is my sword?" Fergus shouted.

"You may have the ax," said Hoth.

"But what will you defend yourself with?"

"There is to be no defending ourselves. That is the agreement."

Fergus thought for a moment. "You are sure that I understand you?" he asked. "I am to cut off your head now. Then tomorrow night you are to cut off my head?"

"That is it."

"There'll be no sending someone else and having him say he is to do it for you?"

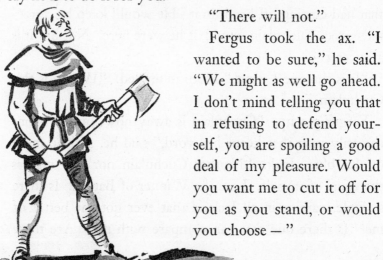

"There will not."

Fergus took the ax. "I wanted to be sure," he said. "We might as well go ahead. I don't mind telling you that in refusing to defend yourself, you are spoiling a good deal of my pleasure. Would you want me to cut it off for you as you stand, or would you choose — "

"You can please yourself," said Hoth.

"You're very obliging," Fergus said politely. He felt the blade of the ax. "That is certainly a grand edge. If it is all the same with you, then let someone get a block of wood. You might as well be comfortable."

So a block of wood was brought, and Hoth knelt down and stretched his neck across it.

"And I to cut off your head tomorrow night," he rumbled, in his voice like thunder.

"Aye," said Fergus, and he winked at the other knights, who were watching very closely. Then Fergus swung the ax high in the air, gave it a couple of whirls, and brought it down on Hoth's neck with a mighty stroke that sent the head bounding off into a corner. There it lay with its eyes catching the light of the fire. A log fell over in the fire, so that a sudden flame shone full on Hoth's body.

"It will be no easy matter for him to cut off your head tomorrow," remarked MacRoi, peering down at it. "I well remember the time — "

"You may give me the ax now," said a voice. It was a tired voice, and not so strong as the voices of most of the Ulstermen, but there was something very familiar about it. Fergus looked around quickly to see who was speaking, but there wasn't a sound out of any of the warriors.

"My ax!" repeated the voice. Fergus spun around, and there was the body of Hoth getting up from its knees. It stood for a moment in an uncertain sort of way. Then it seemed to make up its mind, and off it walked to where the head was lying. It picked up the head and tucked it under an arm. That seemed to make Hoth feel better, for, now that he had collected himself again, he came over to Fergus, took his ax, and started for the door.

"Tomorrow night, yours," said Hoth's head from under his arm. Then he pulled the old cowhide around him and lumbered out into the darkness.

Conal, the Victorious

Fergus, the Battle-Winner, sat down with a thud on the block of wood that Hoth only a moment before had finished with.

"Never in all my life," said Red MacRoi, "have I seen anyone do a thing like that. I remember well the time — "

"I wonder where he comes from," interrupted Fergus.

"What Fergus is wondering," said Shane, a brown gloomy man, with a deep gloomy voice, "is whether or not Hoth will come back."

Then Fergus bounded to his feet with a shout. "I've been cheated."

"Cheated?" asked Shane. "How is that?"

"What business had he picking up his head again?" Fergus yelled, walking rapidly up and down the room.

234

"Cheated!" he roared. "That's what I've been. A man has no right to pick up his head, once it has been chopped off." He felt the back of his own neck, and all the anger went out of him, leaving only sorrow.

"I never could do a thing like that," Fergus continued. "I never could." He shook his head. "Not but what it is a fine thing to be able to do. And now what a fine fix I'm in!" He gave a great sigh. "Ah, well," said he, "I'm a man who keeps his agreements anyway." And with that he went out.

But when the next night came, there wasn't a sign of Fergus, the Battle-Winner. There was the fire blazing in the huge fireplace, and there was Red MacRoi sitting in front of it. There were ever so many others of the great fighting men of Ulster. But there was no sign of Fergus anywhere.

There was a great deal of talk, too, about Fergus. And right in the middle of it all who should arrive but Conal, the Victorious! He was a big stout man with fair hair like a bushel basket on top of his head.

MacRoi nodded to him. "Ah, Conal, so it's you, is it?"

"And have you seen Fergus?" asked Shane.

"I have," replied Conal, "and his chariot was going like the wind. He yelled something about going after a party of Munstermen. I would have offered to go with him, but he kept waving in this direction, so I knew I must be wanted here."

But Conal's words were interrupted by the door bursting open behind him. There stood Hoth, with his head back on his shoulders and his yellow eyes looking hungrier than ever, and his old cowhide pulled around him, and his ax hanging awkwardly in his hand.

"I am a man who keeps his agreements," said Hoth. "Are you?"

"Am I?" roared Conal. "Am I, indeed? Am I not the plague of our enemies and the hope of our friends? Am I not — "

"It is a good thing you are," said Hoth, "for if that is the truth, maybe I could make an agreement with you and have you keep it."

"Keep it!" shouted Conal. "Of course I would keep it. Am I not the greatest in all Ulster? Why, for one little stone off the ground I would cut your head off this very moment!"

"That is the agreement I would make with you," said Hoth in his slow, tired voice.

236

"What agreement?"

"You to cut off my head tonight, and I to cut off yours tomorrow night. Would you keep that agreement?"

Conal drew his sword with a grand flourish.

"Would I?"

"I am to cut off your head tomorrow night," Hoth warned him.

"So you are!" Conal laughed as he whirled his great sword in the air and brought it across Hoth's neck like a flash of light.

"Ha!" sneered Conal. "He'll be no trouble to anyone now." And he turned his back and started to walk off. But he hadn't gone far before he noticed the queer hush that was upon everyone. He turned and saw Hoth's body getting up on its knees.

"You could have used my ax," said Hoth's head, "only you were in such a hurry." And Hoth's body picked up the head, put it carefully under his arm, and walked out. With a slow sort of dignity he walked, too. It was easy to see that Hoth didn't altogether like the way he had been hurried.

"Tomorrow night, yours," said the bloody head.

Conal, the Victorious, one of the greatest of all Knights of Ulster in the Red Branch, sat down as if his knees had been cut from under him. Every single hair in his bushy beard was standing as straight as a young pine tree.

When the next night came, there was no sign either of Fergus, the Battle-Winner, or of Conal, the Victorious. Back came Hoth, the same as before, with his yellow eyes gleaming, his old cowhide wrapped about him, and his ax in his hand. There was a great gathering of knights around the fireplace, but, when Hoth frowned at them, there was nothing but silence.

"Well?" said Hoth in his rumbling voice.

"Aye," said MacRoi. "It is a cold night, for a fact."

"Never mind the cold," snapped Hoth. "What about the agreement I made?"

"You made no agreement with me," MacRoi said, his beard sticking out like the bowsprit of a ship.

"I would, though," Hoth offered, "if I thought you would keep it."

MacRoi smiled politely. "I would be glad to oblige you, but I promised to go to Kerry tomorrow. And I'm a great man to keep my promises. There has never been a time when anyone could say — "

That was as far as MacRoi got. The door burst open with a slam that was three times as great as any slam it ever had made before. And into the room bounded a small, dark man in a gorgeous purple cloak.

"Cuchulain himself!" exclaimed Shane.

There stood Cuchulain, eyeing them all, his sword in his hand. His sword had a hilt of gold, and a point that would bend back to the hilt. Its blade could cut a hair on water or a man in half so swiftly that the one half wouldn't know when the other half had gone from it.

"Look here, Cuchulain," said MacRoi, "they tell me a party of our enemies has been seen over beyond Kerry. Wouldn't it be a good thing for you to run them out?"

"Conal has gone after them," answered Cuchulain.

"Conal?"

"Aye. I met him, and he told me that some stranger was here, saying — "

Hoth walked in front of him. "It was I," he said.

"It was, was it?" shouted Cuchulain. "Defend yourself then!" And he whirled his great sword around his head.

Hoth leaned on his ax, and stood there facing Cuchulain. "I have no need for defense," said he, "so long as you'll keep your agreements."

At that a red flush came to Cuchulain's face and his cheeks glowed, and his eyes shone with the warrior's flame that would come upon him in moments of anger.

"Never," he shouted, "has an agreement of mine gone unkept. Never have I turned my back on an enemy or on a friend, although whole armies avoid me. Forty heads with one stroke of my sword can I — "

"Cuchulain!" cried MacRoi. "I wouldn't — "

"What do I care whether you would or not?" Cuchulain whirled on MacRoi. "Forty heads with a single stroke — "

"It is an agreement with you that I want," interrupted Hoth, "if you'll keep it."

"Keep it?" roared Cuchulain, who was on fire with anger. "Keep it? I'll keep any agreement with anyone anywhere. Take your ax and defend yourself!"

"There's no need for that," replied Hoth softly. "You can cut off my head now, if you'll agree to let me cut off yours tomorrow night. That's all — "

Before anyone could say another word there was a flash like that of lightning. And there was Cuchulain letting the point of his sword come to rest on the ground, and

there was Hoth standing in front of him swaying on his feet, as if a strong wind had struck him. He put one hand up to his neck, did Hoth, and he felt it. Yet he could feel nothing amiss. But when he tried to turn his head, it rolled off his shoulders and tumbled to the ground.

"Oh, Cuchulain! Cuchulain!" groaned MacRoi. "How often have I warned you about your hasty temper!"

Cuchulain looked from one to the other, puzzling over the way that they were behaving, until he happened to look down at the body of Hoth, which was busy picking up its head. Cuchulain stood as if suddenly turned to stone.

Hoth took the head and put it under his arm, as he had done twice before, although he seemed to be more tired than ever this time. His feet dragged as he walked toward the door, and his hand shook, and he nearly dropped his ax as he drew the old cowhide around him.

"Tomorrow night, your head," said Hoth's head as he went out.

"Oh, Cuchulain! Cuchulain!" groaned Shane, the dark, gloomy man. "Will you ever — will you look at what you have done!"

"Maybe Hoth will not come back," said MacRoi. "After all, a man can't go on getting his head cut off. There must be an end to it sometime. He'll wear out. I remember well — "

Cuchulain looked at them all in great amazement.

"It is the first time I ever saw a man pick up his own head," he said, "and hundreds of heads have fallen at my feet."

"He has done it twice before."

"Twice before?"

"Aye! Both Fergus and Conal cut off Hoth's head, but neither of them came back for their part of the agreement. So there is no need of your — "

"I shall be here," said Cuchulain. He drew his purple cloak around him and took a couple of steps toward the door. Then he stopped. "In fact, I'll stay here," he said.

"Now, Cuchulain, listen to me," began MacRoi. "You didn't rightly know how this was going to turn out. How could you? What right has a man to put his head back on again, after you cut it off so beautifully? And it was off. I couldn't have cut it off better myself. Besides — "

Cuchulain waved him away. "It makes no difference," he said. "My agreement must be kept. I shall be here."

And he was, too, the very next night, when Hoth came in with his swirl of snow and the cold wind that caused everyone to move closer to the fire. Right in the center of Warrior's Hall stood Cuchulain, waiting until Hoth lumbered up to him with his old cowhide steaming in the warm air, and his yellow eyes burning as if there were a fire raging inside of him.

242

"So you're here!" said Hoth.

"I am." Cuchulain's voice was very quiet.

"Ah," said MacRoi, "this is a bad day that is come upon us. Why did it have to be Cuchulain himself that must be taken from us in all the greatness of his fame? Go and tell the King the way things are, Shane."

So Shane went to the Royal Chamber and told the King all that had happened. The King hurried to Warrior's Hall, his full-moon face looking pale. For Shane had left nothing out, even in so hasty a telling of the story.

There they were then, all gathered in the Warrior's Hall, the King and MacRoi and many of the greatest men of Ulster. Cuchulain stood sad and alone by a big block of wood. Hoth stood at his side.

"Oh, Cuchulain," cried the King, "is there no way out?"

"There is not," answered Cuchulain, "though I wish there were." And he looked all around the great hall, with its glow of lights and its deep shadows and the great shields of silver and bronze hanging on the walls.

"There is no way out," he continued, "for, when a man like me gives his word, that is the end of the matter."

Then he turned to Hoth. "Is there anything keeping you?" he asked.

"There is not," said Hoth, "unless it be the need of having you kneel down."

243

So Cuchulain knelt down and put his head across the block of wood, so that his neck was a fair invitation to the ax.

Hoth watched him for a moment, then he walked all around him. "Ah!" said he thoughtfully. Then he took another walk in the other direction. "H'm!" said he.

Hoth took the ax and ran his fingers along the edge of the blade. "It is sharp," he remarked, and his voice was as slow as a chariot being dragged over boulders. "Yet I wonder if it is sharp enough."

"Get on with what you're doing," Cuchulain ordered.

Hoth let the ax drop to the ground, and stood there resting on the handle of it. "You would not want your head cut off with a dull ax, would you?" he asked.

"What do I care? Get on with it!"

"But you ought to care," Hoth warned. "It makes a great difference to a man, when getting his head cut off, whether the ax is sharp or not."

He pulled out a hair from his beard and let it drop across the blade. "It is not dull," he said, as the hair divided itself. "Still, it is not so sharp." Then, after considering it for a while, he said, "Well, maybe it will do. Still, I don't know — "

"Will you get on?" thundered Cuchulain, his face getting redder than flames from his stooping. "How much longer must I wait?"

244

"Your sword was sharp when you used it on my neck,"
said Hoth. "But I think maybe the ax will do. Let me
see now."

He raised the blade over his head and, as he raised it,
he seemed to lengthen the way a shadow lengthens as the
sun goes down. He raised it so high that the head of it
struck the very beams of the roof. For a moment he held
it there, and the red light of the fire gleamed on its edge.
So great was the silence that even the logs in their blazing

ceased to crackle. Then Hoth brought the ax down. In a mighty sweep it came, like a bolt falling out of the sky. Only he turned the blade so that, instead of striking Cuchulain, it went past him, and the head of the ax struck the floor. It struck with such force that every man in the hall was shaken almost out of his seat.

Cuchulain remained kneeling by the block of wood, with his neck resting upon it and his head bowed at the farther side of it.

"Ah, well," said Hoth, and his voice sounded a little less tired now, "you can get up, Cuchulain. You are the one man that kept his agreement with me, so you had better keep your head where it belongs. It is too good a head to have rolling about on the ground. Indeed, there are few men who would rather lose their heads than break their promises."

Hoth looked around him with a slow look. "A kingdom," said he, "cannot last long when the agreements of its people are broken."

He looked at the King, who was frowning angrily, but MacRoi was chuckling softly to himself.

Then Hoth pulled his old cowhide around him. "I'm going back to Dun Curoi now," said he.

And by that they knew he was not Hoth at all, but Curoi, famous throughout all Ireland for his magic.

Robert M. Hyatt

246

TO YOUR GOOD HEALTH

Long, long ago there lived a King who was such a mighty monarch that, whenever he sneezed, everyone in the whole country had to say, "To your good health!" Everyone said it except the Shepherd with the bright blue eyes, and he would not say it.

The King heard of this and was very angry, and sent for the Shepherd to appear before him.

The Shepherd came and stood before the throne, where the King sat looking very grand and powerful. But however grand or powerful he might be, the Shepherd did not feel a bit afraid of him.

"Say at once, 'To my good health'!" cried the King.

"To my good health," replied the Shepherd.

"To mine — to mine, you rascal!" stormed the King.

"To mine, to mine, Your Majesty," was the answer.

"But to mine — to my own!" roared the King, and beat on his breast in a rage.

"Well, yes — to mine, of course, to my own," cried the Shepherd, and gently tapped his breast.

The King was so beside himself with anger that he could not speak.

The Lord Chamberlain took the Shepherd by the arm

and whispered in his ear, "Say at once — this very moment, 'To your good health, Your Majesty,' for if you don't say it, you will lose your life."

"No, I won't say it till I get the Princess for my wife," was the Shepherd's answer.

Now the Princess was sitting on a little throne beside the King, her father, and she looked as sweet and lovely as a little golden dove. When she heard what the Shepherd said, she could not help laughing, for the fact is that this young shepherd with the blue eyes pleased her very much. Indeed, he pleased her better than any king's son she had yet seen.

But the King was by no means so pleased as his daughter, and he gave orders to throw the Shepherd into the white bear's pit.

The guards led him away and thrust him into the pit with the white bear, who had had nothing to eat for two days and was very hungry.

The door of the pit was hardly closed when the bear rushed at the Shepherd; but when it saw his eyes, it was so frightened that it was ready to eat itself. It shrank away into a corner and gazed at him from there. In spite of being so hungry, it did not dare to touch him, but sucked its own paws.

The Shepherd felt that if he once took his eyes off the the beast he was a dead man. In order to keep himself awake, he made songs and sang them, and so the night went by.

Next morning the Lord Chamberlain came to the pit, expecting to see the Shepherd's bones, and was amazed to find him alive and well. Once more the Shepherd was led before the King, who said angrily, "Well, you have learned what it is to be very near death. Now will you say, 'To my very good health'?"

But the Shepherd answered, "I am not afraid of ten deaths. I will only say it if I may have the Princess for my wife."

"Then go to your death " cried the King, and ordered him to be thrown into the den with the ten wild boars.

The wild boars had not been fed for a week. When the Shepherd was thrust into their den, they rushed at him to tear him to pieces. But the Shepherd took a little flute out of the sleeve of his jacket, and began to play a merry tune.

At first the wild boars shrank shyly away, and then they stood up on their hind legs and danced gaily. They looked so funny that the Shepherd would have given anything to be able to laugh, but he dared not stop playing, for he knew well enough that the moment he stopped, they would fall upon him and tear him to pieces. His eyes were of no use to him here, for he could not stare ten wild boars in the face at once.

So he kept on playing and the wild boars kept on dancing. By degrees he played faster and faster, till they could hardly twist and turn quickly enough. They ended by all falling over one another in a heap, quite exhausted and out of breath.

Then the Shepherd dared to laugh at last. He laughed so long and so loud that when the Lord Chamberlain came early in the morning, expecting to find only his bones, the tears were still running down his cheeks from laughter.

As soon as the King was dressed, he had the Shepherd again brought before him. He was more angry than ever to think the wild boars had not torn the Shepherd to bits, and he said, "Well, you have learned how it feels to be near ten deaths. Now say, 'To my good health'!"

But the Shepherd broke in, "I do not fear a hundred deaths. I will only say it if I may have the Princess for my wife."

"Then go to a hundred deaths!" roared the King, and

he ordered the Shepherd to be thrown down the well of scythes.

The guards dragged him away to a dark dungeon, in the middle of which was a deep well with one hundred sharp scythes all round it. At the bottom of the well was a little light by which one could see whether anyone who had been thrown in had fallen to the bottom.

When the Shepherd was dragged to the dungeon, he begged the guards to leave him alone a little while, so that he might look down into the pit of scythes. Perhaps he might, after all, make up his mind to say, "To your good health" to the King.

When the guards had left him alone, he stuck up his long stick near the wall, hung his cloak round the stick, and put his hat on the top. He also hung his knapsack up inside the cloak, so that it might seem to have some body within it. When this was done, he called out to the guards and said that he had considered the matter, but after all he could not say what the King wished.

The guards came in, threw the hat and cloak, knapsack and stick all down in the well together. They watched to see whether they put out the light at the bottom, and then came away, thinking that now there was really an end of the Shepherd. But he had hidden in a dark corner, and was laughing to himself all the time.

Quite early next morning the Lord Chamberlain came

with a lamp, and he nearly fell backwards with surprise when he saw the prisoner still alive and well. Once more the Shepherd was brought before the King, who was now more angry than ever.

"Well," cried the King, "now you have been near a hundred deaths. Will you say, 'To your good health'?"

But the Shepherd only gave the same answer, "I won't say it till the Princess is my wife."

"Perhaps, after all, you may do it for less," said the King, who saw that there was no chance of killing the Shepherd. His life seemed to be protected by magic. So the King ordered the state coach to be got ready. Then he told the Shepherd to get in and sit beside him, and ordered the coachman to drive to the silver wood.

When they reached it, he said, "Do you see this silver wood? Well, if you will say, 'To your good health,' I will give it to you."

The Shepherd turned hot and cold by turns, but he still made the same answer, "I will not say it till the Princess is my wife."

The King was angry, but he did not give up. He drove farther on till they came to a splendid castle, all of gold.

"Do you see this golden castle?" he said. "Well, I will give you that, too, both the silver wood and the golden castle, if only you will say that one thing to me, 'To your good health.'"

The Shepherd was quite dazzled but he still said, "No, I will not say it till I have the Princess for my wife."

This time the King was overcome with grief, and gave orders to drive on to the diamond pond. There he tried once more, saying, "You shall have them all — all, if you will but say, 'To your good health.'"

The Shepherd had to shut his blue eyes tight not to be dazzled with the bright pond, but still he said, "No, no! I will not say it till I have the Princess for my wife."

Then the King saw that he might as well give in and so he said, "Well, well, it is all the same to me. I will give you my daughter to wife, but then you really and truly must say to me, 'To your good health.'"

"Of course I'll say it. Why should I not say it? It stands to reason that I shall say it then."

At this the King was more delighted than anyone could have believed. He made it known all through the country that there was going to be a great feast, as the Princess was going to be married. And everyone was glad to hear that the Princess, who had refused so many royal suitors, had ended by falling in love with the Shepherd with the bright blue eyes.

There was such a wedding as had never before been seen. Everyone ate and drank and danced. Even the sick were feasted, and quite tiny new-born children had presents given them. But the greatest merrymaking was in the King's palace. There the best bands played and the best food was cooked.

And when, according to custom, the great boar's head was brought in and placed before the King, so that he might carve it, the delightful smell was so strong that the King began to sneeze with all his might.

"To your very good health!" cried the Shepherd before anyone else, and the King was so pleased that he did not regret having given him his daughter.

In time, when the old King died, the Shepherd came to the throne. He made a very good king, and never expected his people to wish him well against their wills. All the same, everyone did wish him well, because they loved him.

Andrew Lang

ALI BABA AND THE FORTY THIEVES

THE ROBBERS' CAVE

IN a town in Persia there lived two brothers, the sons of a poor man. One was named Cassim, and the other, Ali Baba. Cassim, the elder, married a wife with a considerable fortune, and lived in a handsome house with plenty of servants. The wife of Ali Baba was as poor as himself. They lived in a small cottage in the suburbs of the city, and he supported his family by cutting wood in a neighboring forest.

One day, when Ali Baba was in the forest, and was preparing to load his asses with the wood he had cut, he saw a troop of horsemen coming toward him. Believing them to be robbers, he hastily climbed a large thick tree which stood near a rock, and hid among the branches.

The horsemen soon galloped up to the rock and dismounted. Ali Baba counted forty of them. Each took a heavily loaded pack from his horse. He who seemed to be their captain, turning to the rock, said, "Open Sesame." Immediately a door opened in the rock, and as soon as all the robbers had passed in, the door shut itself.

In a short time the door opened once more, and the

robbers came out, followed by their captain, who said, "Shut Sesame." The door closed, and the troop, mounting their horses, were presently out of sight.

Ali Baba remained in the tree a long time to make sure that the robbers did not return. Then he climbed down, and, approaching the rock, said, "Open Sesame." Immediately the door flew open, and Ali Baba beheld an enormous cave, very light, and filled with all sorts of rich merchandise and with heaps of gold and silver coin which these robbers had taken from merchants and travelers.

Ali Baba went in search of his asses, and having brought them to the rock, put on their backs as many bags of gold coin as they could carry, and covered up the bags with some loose sticks of wood. Afterwards (not forgetting to say "Shut Sesame"), he drove the asses back to the city. There he unloaded them in the stable belonging to his cottage, carried the bags into the house, and spread the gold coins out upon the floor before his wife.

His wife, delighted to possess so much money, wanted to count it. Finding this would take too much time, she decided to measure it. Running to the house of Ali Baba's brother, she entreated his wife to lend her a small measure.

Cassim's wife was very proud and envious. "I wonder," she said to herself, "what sort of grain such poor people can have to measure." So, before she gave the measure, she rubbed the bottom with some suet.

256

Away ran Ali Baba's wife to measure the money. Then, after she had helped her husband to bury it in the yard, she carried back the measure to her brother-in-law's house, without noticing that a piece of gold was left sticking to the bottom of it.

"Fine doings, indeed!" cried Cassim's wife to her husband, when she saw the gold piece. "Your brother, who pretends to be so poor, is richer than you are, for he does not count his money, but measures it."

Cassim, hearing these words, and seeing the piece of gold, grew as envious as his wife. Hastening to his brother, he threatened to inform the Cadi of his wealth, if he did not admit how he came by it. Ali Baba, without hesitation, told him the history of the robbers, and the secret of the cave, and offered him half his treasure.

The envious Cassim was not satisfied. He decided to have fifty times more than that out of the wealth in the robbers' cave. Accordingly, he rose early the next morning, and set out with ten mules loaded with great chests. He found the rock easily enough by Ali Baba's description. Saying "Open Sesame," he entered the cave, where he found even more treasure than he had expected.

He immediately began to gather bags of gold and pieces of rich brocade, all of which he piled close to the door. But when he wanted to get out to load the treasure on his mules, the thought of his wonderful riches had made him entirely forget the word which caused the door to open. He tried "Wheat," "Barley," "Oats," and a thousand others. The door remained as immovable as the rock itself.

Presently he heard the sound of horses' hoofs, which he rightly guessed to be the robbers', and he trembled with fear lest his greed for riches should now cause his death. He determined, however, to make an effort to escape. When he heard the word "Sesame" and saw the door open, he sprang out, but was instantly killed by the swords of the robbers.

The thieves now held a council, but not one of them could possibly guess by what means Cassim had entered the cave. They agreed to cut Cassim's body into four quarters, and hang the pieces within the cave, that it might terrify anyone from further attempts at robbery. They also determined not to return to the cave for some time for fear of being watched.

When Cassim's wife saw night come on, and her husband did not return, she became greatly terrified. She watched at her window till daybreak, and then went to tell Ali Baba of her fears.

Ali Baba drove his asses to the forest without delay. He was alarmed to see blood near the rock. On entering the cave, he found the body of his unfortunate brother cut in quarters and hung up within the door. Taking down the pieces, he put them upon one of his asses and covered them with sticks of wood. Weeping for the miserable end of his brother, he returned to the city. The door of his brother's house was opened by Morgiana, an intelligent, faithful woman slave, who, as Ali Baba knew, could be trusted with the secret.

He therefore delivered the body to Morgiana, and went himself to tell the sad news to the wife of Cassim. The poor woman wept bitterly, and blamed herself for her foolish envy and curiosity, as the cause of her husband's death. Ali Baba told her to dry her tears and to leave everything to Morgiana.

Morgiana, having washed the body, hastened to an apothecary's and asked for a special medicine, saying that it was for her master Cassim, who was dangerously ill. She took care to spread the report of Cassim's illness throughout the neighborhood. As people saw Ali Baba and his wife going daily to the house of their brother in great sadness, they were not surprised to hear shortly that Cassim had died of his illness.

The next difficulty was to bury him without discovery.

Morgiana had a plan for that also. She put on her veil and went to a distant part of the city very early in the morning. There she found a poor cobbler just opening his stall. She put a piece of gold into his hand, and told him he should have another, if he would let himself be blindfolded and go with her, carrying his tools with him.

Mustapha, the cobbler, hesitated at first, but the gold tempted him and he agreed. Then Morgiana, carefully covering his eyes, led him to Cassim's house. Taking him into the room where the body was lying, she removed the bandage from his eyes and bade him sew the mangled limbs together. Mustapha obeyed her order and, having received two pieces of gold, was led blindfold back to his own stall. Morgiana then covered the body with a sheet, sent for the undertaker, and Cassim was buried with all due dignity the same day.

Ali Baba now removed his few goods, and all the gold coin that he had brought home from the cave, to the house of his dead brother, of which he took possession. Cassim's widow received every kind attention from both Ali Baba and his wife, and was glad to have their company.

After an interval of some weeks, the troop of robbers again visited the cave in the forest. They were astonished to find the body had been taken away and that everything else in the cave remained in its usual order.

"We are discovered," said the captain. "Which of you, my brave comrades, will undertake to search out the villain who is in possession of our secret?"

One of the boldest of the troop offered himself and was accepted on the following conditions: if he succeeded in his venture, he was to be made second in command of the troop; but if he failed, he was immediately to be put to death. The bold robber agreed to the conditions, and having disguised himself, he proceeded to the city.

He arrived there about dawn and found the cobbler Mustapha in his stall, which was always open before any other shop in the town.

"Good morrow, friend," said the robber, as he passed the stall. "You rise early. I should think, old as you are, you could scarcely see to work by this light."

"Indeed, sir," replied the cobbler, "old as I am, I do not lack good eyesight. I tell you I sewed a dead body together not so long ago where I had not so good a light as I have now."

262

"A dead body!" exclaimed the robber. "You mean that you sewed up the winding-sheet for a dead body."

"I mean no such thing," replied Mustapha. "I tell you that I sewed the four quarters of a man together."

This was enough to convince the robber that he had luckily met the very man who could give him the information he was seeking. However, he did not wish to appear so eager that he would alarm the cobbler.

"Ha! Ha!" said he. "I find, good Mr. Cobbler, that you realize I am a stranger here, and you wish to make me believe that the people of your city do impossible things."

"I tell you," said Mustapha, in a loud and angry tone, "I sewed a dead body together with my own hands."

"Then I suppose you can tell me also where you performed this wonderful business."

Upon this, Mustapha told how he had been led blindfold to the house, and what had happened there.

"Well, my friend," said the robber, "It's a fine story, but not very easy to believe. However, if you can point out to me the house you talk of, I will give you four pieces of gold to show that I am sorry not to have believed you at first."

"I think," said the cobbler after a while, "that if you were to blindfold me, I should remember every turning we made. With my eyes open, I am sure I should never find the place."

Accordingly, the robber covered Mustapha's eyes with his handkerchief, and the cobbler led him through most of the main streets. At last, stopping by Cassim's door, he said, "Here it is. I went no farther than this house."

The robber immediately marked the door with a piece of chalk, and giving Mustapha his four pieces of gold, let him go. Shortly after the thief and Mustapha had left, Morgiana, coming home from market, noticed the little mark of white chalk on the door. Suspecting something was wrong, she marked four doors on one side and five on the other of her master's in exactly the same manner, without saying a word to anyone.

The robber meantime returned to his troop, and boasted greatly of his success. His captain and comrades praised him. Arming themselves well, they traveled to the town in different disguises, and in groups of three or four.

It was agreed among them that they were to meet in the market-place in the evening. The captain and the robber who had discovered the house were to go there first, to find out to whom it belonged. When they arrived and began to examine the doors by the light of a lantern, they found, to their confusion and astonishment, that ten doors were marked exactly alike. The robber, who was the captain's guide, could not explain this mystery. So, when the disappointed troop got back to the forest, he was put to death.

Another now offered himself upon the same conditions. He went to town, and having bribed Mustapha, discovered the house, and made a mark with some dark-red chalk upon the door in a part where it would not be easily noticed. Also he examined carefully the surrounding doors, to be certain that no such marks were upon them. But nothing could escape the sharp eyes of Morgiana. Scarcely had the robber left, when she discovered the red mark. Getting some red chalk, she marked seven doors on each side, in exactly the same place and in the same manner.

The next evening the robber triumphantly brought his captain to the spot. Great, indeed, was his confusion and dismay when he found it impossible to say which, among fifteen houses marked exactly alike, was the right one.

The captain, furious with disappointment, returned again with the troop to the forest, and the second robber was also put to death.

The Brave Morgiana

The captain, having lost two of his troop, decided to go himself upon the business. First, he went to the cobbler Mustapha, who, for six pieces of gold, gladly performed the same services for him as he had for the other two strangers. Wiser than his men, the captain did not risk a mark upon the door, but carefully studied the house, counted the number of windows, and passed by it very often, to be certain that he should know it again.

He then returned to the forest, and ordered his troop to go into the town and buy nineteen mules and thirty-eight large jars, one full of oil and the rest empty. In two or three days the jars were bought, and all things were ready. The captain put a man, properly armed, into each jar. He rubbed the jars on the outside with oil and had holes bored in the covers for the men to breathe through.

Then he loaded his mules, and in the disguise of an oil-merchant, entered the town in the early evening. He drove to the street where Ali Baba lived, and found him sitting at the door of his house.

"Sir," said he to Ali Baba, "I have brought this oil a great way to sell, and am too late for this day's market. Since I am a stranger in this town, will you do me the favor to let me put my mules in your courtyard, and direct me where I may lodge tonight?"

Ali Baba, who was a very good-natured man, welcomed the pretended oil-merchant most kindly, and offered him a bed in his own house. He ordered the mules to be unloaded in the yard and properly fed, and then invited his guest in to supper.

The captain, having seen the jars placed ready in the yard, followed Ali Baba into the house, and after supper was shown to the guest chamber.

It happened that Morgiana had to sit up later that night than usual, to get ready her master's bathing linen for the following morning. While she was busy about the fire, her lamp went out. There was no more oil in the house.

After considering what she could possibly do for a light, she remembered the thirty-eight oil jars in the yard, and determined to take a little oil out of one of them for her lamp. As she approached the first jar, the robber within said, "Is it time, captain?"

Any other slave, on hearing a man in an oil jar, would have screamed out, but Morgiana instantly controlled herself, and replied softly, "No, not yet. Lie still till I call you." She passed on to every jar, receiving the same question and making the same answer, till she came to the last, which was really filled with oil.

Morgiana was now certain that this was a scheme to kill her master, Ali Baba. So she ran back to the kitchen, and brought out a large kettle, which she filled with oil and set on a great wood fire. As soon as it boiled she went and poured into the jars enough boiling oil to kill every man within them. Having done this, she put out her fire and her lamp, and crept softly to her chamber.

The captain of the robbers, when everything was quiet in the house, arose and went down into the yard to collect his men. Coming to the first jar, he noticed the steam of the boiled oil. He ran hastily to the rest, and found every one of his troop put to death in the same manner. Full of rage and hopelessness, he forced the lock of a door that led into the garden and made his escape over the walls.

On the following morning, Morgiana told her master, Ali Baba, of his wonderful escape from the pretended oil-merchant and his gang of robbers. Ali Baba at first could scarcely believe her tale, but when he saw the robbers dead in the jars, he could not praise her cleverness and courage enough.

Without letting anyone else into the secret, he and Morgiana the next night buried the thirty-seven thieves in a deep trench at the bottom of the garden. The jars and mules, as he had no use for them, were sent from time to time to the different markets and sold.

The captain returned to his cave, and for some time gave himself up to grief and hopelessness. At length, however, he determined once more to destroy Ali Baba. He removed by degrees some of the valuable goods from the cave to the city, and took a shop exactly opposite to Ali Baba's house. He furnished this shop with everything that was rare and costly, and went by the name of the merchant Cogia Hassan.

Many persons admired his goods. Among others, Ali Baba's son went every day to the shop. The pretended Cogia Hassan soon appeared to be very fond of Ali Baba's son, offered him many presents, and often invited him to dinner.

Ali Baba's son thought it was only polite to make some return for these kindnesses and begged his father to invite Cogia Hassan to supper. Ali Baba made no objection, and the invitation was accordingly given.

A most excellent supper was planned. Morgiana cooked it in the best manner, and as was her custom, she carried in the first dish herself. The moment she looked at Cogia Hassan, she knew he was the pretended oil-merchant. The cautious Morgiana did not say a word to anyone of this discovery, but sent the other slaves into the kitchen, and waited at table herself. While Cogia Hassan was drinking, she noticed he had a dagger hid under his coat.

When supper was ended, and the dessert on the table, Morgiana went away and dressed herself as a dancing-girl. She next called Abdalla, a fellow slave, to play while she danced. As soon as she appeared at the door, her master, who was very fond of seeing her dance, ordered her to come in to entertain his guest with some of her best dancing.

Morgiana danced several dances; and then drawing a dagger from her girdle, she performed many surprising things with it, sometimes presenting the point to one and sometimes to another, and then seemed to strike it into her own bosom.

Suddenly she paused, and holding the dagger in the right hand, presented her left to her master as if begging some money. Upon which Ali Baba and his son each gave her a small piece of money. She then turned to the pretended Cogia Hassan, and while he was putting his hand into his purse, she plunged the dagger into his heart.

"Wretch!" cried Ali Baba. "You have ruined me and my family."

"No, sir," replied Morgiana, "I have saved you and your son. Look well at this man, and you will find him to be the

pretended oil-merchant who came once before to rob and
murder you."

Ali Baba, having pulled off the turban and the cloak
which the false Cogia Hassan wore, soon discovered that
he was not only the pretended oil-merchant, but the captain of the forty robbers who had slain his brother Cassim.
There was no doubt that his purpose had been to kill
Ali Baba, and probably his son, with the hidden dagger.

Ali Baba, full of gratitude to Morgiana for thus saving his life a second time, turned to her and said, "My

dear Morgiana, I gladly give you your freedom, but that is not enough. I will also marry you to my son, who can admire you no less than does his father."

The son joyfully accepted his bride, having long felt a warm affection for the good slave, Morgiana.

That night they buried the captain in the trench, along with his troop of robbers. A few days afterwards, Ali Baba celebrated the marriage of his son and Morgiana with a magnificent feast. Everyone who knew Morgiana said she was worthy of her good fortune, and praised her master's kindness.

For a year Ali Baba stayed away from the cave in the forest, but at length his curiosity led him to make another journey.

When he came to the cave he saw no footsteps of either men or horses. Speaking the magic words, "Open Sesame," he went in. He guessed by the state of things in the cave that no one had been there since the pretended Cogia Hassan had set up his shop in the city.

Ali Baba took home as much gold as his horse could carry. Later he took his son to the cave and taught him the secret. This secret they handed down to their descendants. Using their good fortune with care, they lived in honor and splendor, and served with dignity some of the chief offices in the city.

From THE ARABIAN NIGHTS

THE ADMIRAL'S GHOST

I TELL you a tale tonight
    Which a seaman told to me,
With eyes that gleamed in the lanthorn light
    And a voice as low as the sea.

You could almost hear the stars
    Twinkling up in the sky,
And the old wind woke and moaned in the spars,
    And the same old waves went by,

Singing the same old song
    As ages and ages ago,
While he froze my blood in that deep-sea night
    With the things that he seemed to know.

A bare foot pattered on deck;
    Ropes creaked; then — all grew still,
And he pointed his finger straight in my face
    And growled, as a sea-dog will.

"Do 'ee know who Nelson was?
    That pore little shriveled form
With the patch on his eye and the pinned-up sleeve
    And a soul like a North Sea storm?

273

"Ask of the Devonshire men!
    They know, and they'll tell you true;
He wasn't the pore little chawed-up chap
    That Hardy thought he knew.

"He wasn't the man you think!
    His patch was a dern disguise!
For he knew that they'd find him out, d'you see,
    If they looked him in both his eyes.

"He was twice as big as he seemed,
    But his clothes were cunningly made.
He'd both of his hairy arms all right!
    The sleeve was a trick of the trade.

"You've heard of sperrits, no doubt;
    Well, there's more in the matter than that!
But he wasn't the patch and he wasn't the sleeve,
    And he wasn't the laced cocked-hat.

"Nelson was just — a ghost!
    You may laugh! But the Devonshire men
They knew that he'd come when England called,
    And they know that he'll come again.

"I'll tell you the way it was
    (For none of the landsmen know),
And to tell it you right, you must go a-starn
    Two hundred years or so.

.   .   .   .

"The waves were lapping and slapping
    The same as they are today;
And Drake lay dying aboard his ship
    In Nombre Dios Bay.

"The scent of the foreign flowers
    Came floating all around;
'But I'd give my soul for the smell o' the pitch,'
    Says he, 'in Plymouth Sound.'

" 'What shall I do,' he says,
    'When the guns begin to roar,
An' England wants me, and me not there
    To shatter 'er foes once more?'

"You've heard what he said, maybe,
    But I'll mark you the p'ints again;
For I want you to box your compass right
    And get my story plain.

" 'You must take my drum,' he says,
    'To the old sea-wall at home;
And if ever you strike that drum,' he says,
    'Why, strike me blind, I'll come!

" 'If England needs me, dead
    Or living, I'll rise that day!
I'll rise from the darkness under the sea
    Ten thousand miles away.'

"That's what he said, and he died;
    An' his pirates, listenin' roun'
With their crimson doublets and jeweled swords
    That flashed as the sun went down,

"They sewed him up in his shroud
    With a round-shot top and toe,
To sink him under the salt sharp sea
    Where all good seamen go.

"They lowered him down in the deep,
    And there in the sunset light
They boomed a broadside over his grave,
    As meanin' to say 'Good night.'

"They sailed away in the dark
    To the dear little isle they knew;
And they hung his drum by the old sea-wall
    The same as he told them to.

     .   .   .   .

"Two hundred years went by,
    And the guns began to roar,
And England was fighting hard for her life,
    As ever she fought of yore.

" 'It's only my dead that count,'
    She said, as she says today.
'It isn't the ships and it isn't the guns
    'Ull sweep Trafalgar's Bay.'

"D'you guess who Nelson was?
   You may laugh, but it's true as true!
There was more in that pore little chawed-up chap
   Than ever his best friend knew.

"The foe was creepin' close,
   In the dark, to our white-cliffed isle;
They were ready to leap at England's throat,
   When — oh, you may smile, you may smile!

"But — ask of the Devonshire men;
   For they heard in the dead of night
The roll of a drum, and they saw him pass
   On a ship all shining white.

"He stretched out his dead cold face
   And he sailed in the grand old way!
The fishes had taken an eye and his arm,
   But he swept Trafalgar's Bay.

"Nelson — was Francis Drake!
   Oh, what matters the uniform,
Or the patch on your eye or your pinned-up sleeve,
   If your soul's like a North Sea storm?"

                                        Alfred Noyes

BOYS WHO FOUND OUT

THE LAZY WATER CARRIER

MENES was lazy. So his mother said, and so all the neighbors said. They pitied her for having such a lazy son. Menes did not think he was lazy. He just did not like to work. So he was always thinking up ways to keep from working.

When he was a little boy, playing by the river, no one had thought him lazy. He was always working with sticks and stones, building dams to hold the water back and ditches to carry it where he wanted it. He made boats of sticks fastened together with reeds and shaped them so cleverly that they always went faster than those of the other boys. His mother had been proud of him in those days. Once the priest, walking by the river bank and watching him at play, had stopped as he passed her on his way home and told her that she had a bright boy.

280

What the priest had thought in his heart was, "A pity that he must always be a water carrier!" But he did not say that aloud, for that was one of the things that no one, not even a priest, would say aloud in ancient Egypt. Menes's father had been a water carrier, and his grandfather and his great-grandfather, as far back as anyone could remember. So Menes must be a water carrier, too, and that was where the trouble came.

When Menes was big enough to go to work, he went to the carpenter, who fitted on his shoulders a wooden yoke or frame, on which could be hung two pails. Now Menes was ready to hire out to the rich man of the village, who would give him food and clothes in return for carrying water all day long.

At first Menes was proud of his new work. He learned to balance his yoke skillfully so that he could fill the pails almost to the rim and still not lose a drop of water as he climbed the path from the river. He walked quickly and counted "one, two, three" for the trips he made from the house to the river. Then he began to count "one, two, three" over again, for that was as high as anyone knew how to count in those days. The servants of the house were pleased with the quickness with which the new boy brought the water.

But that did not last long. To play with the yoke and the pails for a day or a week was all very well. But when he had done it for all the days between two moons, Menes was ready for something else. But there was nothing else for him to do. He was a water carrier, the son of a water carrier.

The servants began to complain of the length of time that it took him to go to the river and come back.

"My pots go dry and burn while that lazy boy plays by the river," complained the cook.

"And my washing stands waiting for the jars to be filled," complained another woman.

Word came to his mother, and she scolded him, and he promised to do better. But in a few days it was the same old story again. He had stopped by the river to watch the boys at play, or he had fallen asleep while the pails were filling.

"But, Mother," he would say, when she begged him to do his work better or he would lose his job, "what if I do lose this job? Is there not something else I can do? Am I to carry pails of water up and down that bank all my life?"

He was. That was all there was to it. He was a water carrier, because he was the son of a water carrier, and he was to carry water all his life. When he became a man, he would probably not carry water to the houses. He might sit by the stream and swing it up all day in a basket on a rope to fill the ditches that watered the fields.

"At least then I could sit still," thought Menes, as he walked back and forth in the sun, with the wooden yoke cutting into his shoulders.

He did not really want to sit still, for he was not really so lazy as he seemed. But he did not like to do the same work hour after hour, day after day.

"This yoke," he said to the other water carriers, "is like the yoke the oxen wear as they plow the fields. Are we no better than oxen that we should wear yokes and carry loads?"

But still he must wear his yoke and fill his jars.

He tried all sorts of ways of filling them. Sometimes he took them off the ropes and leaned over the river and dipped them, one by one, into the current. Or he slipped the yoke off his sore shoulders and tipped it, so that one end of it hung low, and then dipped the jar into the water.

"Any way for a change," he said to himself, as he made his way back and forth from house to river and river to house.

The other carriers always went to the same place. But one day, after his work was done, Menes found a new deep pool where the bank curved out and held the water back. It would be easier to get water here, for the current was less swift. Besides, it was nearer the house.

"Why do we never get water here?" he asked another carrier, telling him of this place.

"Because we have always drawn it from the other place," replied the man. "Probably it is too deep here."

But a new place was just what Menes wanted. He was tired already of the old one, though he had been there for only one moon, while the older carrier had been there for many, many moons. The next day he went back to the new place. The water was deep. He could not reach down to dip the pail in. But by letting his yoke down as if it were a fishing pole, he could fill the pail. Pulling the full pail up on the yoke was hard, but he went back and tried it again. This time he steadied the yoke on a rock, so that it should not slip, as it had on the soft earth. It came up more easily, with the rock to hold it.

Next day Menes took a fishing pole from home and tried to balance the pail on that. Anyone who had seen him then would not have thought him a dull, lazy boy. But his efforts with the pole and the rocks kept him too long at the pool.

"It is no use," said the man who hired the rich man's servants, when he heard that Menes had been late again and again. "The boy is lazy and will not work."

That night he told Menes not to come any more, for there were other boys ready to draw the water and bring it quickly.

Menes was sorry when his mother cried because he had lost his job, but he could not care very much himself.

284

He was glad to have time to go back to the pool and work with his pole and rocks. He was sure he could find a way to draw the water up more quickly and easily.

Day after day went by while Menes worked at the pool. Each morning, at his mother's wish, he went out and tried to find a new job. But no one would hire him for a house servant, for the story had spread that he was lazy. At last a farmer who had known his father and was sorry for his mother told Menes that he might come and work on a corner of his land, digging ditches and filling them with water. Here Menes worked all day alone, with no one to watch him.

One day the farmer, looking out at noonday when no one worked in the hot sunshine, saw Menes going back and forth in this distant field. He was so surprised that he walked over toward the field and stood and watched the boy for a time, before Menes knew that he was there. The ditches were dug, and Menes was filling them with

water, but he was not dipping the pails by hand in the old way, or swinging a basket on a rope. His pail was fastened to the end of a pole which rested on a pile of rocks. The long end of the pole, with the pail on it, hung out over the river. Menes leaned his own weight on the short end. The pail swung up quickly. Menes emptied the water out of it and swung it back again.

"See," shouted Menes, when he saw the farmer coming, "I have just got it to working. Look and see how easily the water comes up."

The boy was so eager and excited that the farmer took the end of the pole from him, as he begged him to, and lifted the pail while Menes guided it. He had thought he would have to push hard on the end of the pole, for he knew how heavy a pail of water is and saw how far it had to be lifted. But to his surprise, the pole came up easily and quickly with its load. There was none of the back-breaking pull of which the water carriers complained when they had to dip water from a deep ditch.

The farmer went in haste to the head man of the village to bring him to see how Menes worked his pole. Other water carriers came to see it and rigged up poles of their own. There was no more talk of Menes being lazy, for with his pole he could lift water faster, as well as more easily, than any other man by the old ways.

Marion F. Lansing

286

THE PARCHMENT DOOR

NEPHEW OF ROLAND

THREE young riders carefully guided their small sturdy horses, one behind the other, along the path through the woods. Suddenly, the long howl of a wolf came from somewhere in the shadowed forest about them.

Bernard, leading the way, drew in his rein so sharply that his horse reared. Little Gisela, close behind him, gave a gasp and turned, looking fearfully over her shoulder. Alain, last of the three, could see how white her face had grown, how frightened her blue eyes. Alain's own heart had begun to thump, but he urged his horse forward until he caught up with his small cousin.

"Don't be afraid, Gisela. The three of us, mounted as we are, have nothing to fear from a single wolf."

Even as he spoke, an answering howl came from another part of the forest — then more. The horses snorted and jerked their ears first in one direction, then in another.

Bernard, heavy and blond and taller by a head than his cousin, slight dark-haired Alain, turned his horse about and circled back.

"Ride on, both of you!" he ordered, his voice sharp and strained. "Alain, you take the lead. It sounds to me

like the gathering of a pack. Once we are out of the forest they'll not dare to follow us. But since the rear is the place of greatest danger, I had best be the one to guard it."

Alain's face flushed, and his gray eyes sparkled with anger. After all, Bernard, in spite of his larger size, was no older than he. But in the face of danger from wolves, he knew this was hardly the time for a quarrel. Sternly he set his lips and rode on to take his place at the head of the little procession.

In a few moments they had reached the edge of the forest. The wolves, still unseen, were left behind. Before the three riders lay a grassy valley, from the center of which rose a steep, rocky knoll. On this slight rise,

288

surrounded by a deep ditch and a wall of pointed timbers,
stood the high, square tower of logs with its surrounding
buildings, which was their home. The houses were roofed
with straw and chinked with stones and clay, but they
were the dwelling of a great man. Gerhard, father of
Bernard and Gisela, ruled these marshes of Brittany in the
name of the king of the Franks, Charlemagne.

The ponies galloped down the smooth pasture slope.
On the rim of the hills across the valley the sunset lin-
gered, then suddenly was gone. From many different
directions came flocks and herds for the night's shelter.
They were driven by close-cropped peasant boys, barefooted and dressed in skins or the roughest of woven
cloth.

Up the dusty road between the peasant huts, over the
echoing boards of the drawbridge, the horses clattered,
home at last! And there the three young riders stopped
suddenly in surprise, forgetting danger and quarrels both.
Strange horses — Alain counted a dozen of them — were

being groomed by the stable boys. From the wide-open doorway of the great hall came the sound of many voices.

Gisela slipped down from her saddle. "Strangers!" she cried. "Who can they be?" Together the three hurried into the hall.

As Alain's eyes became used to the dark, smoky interior, he saw that there were many tall strangers seated on the benches about the blazing fire. Still others sat at the high table with Count Gerhard and his countess, and Alain's own mother, the widowed Lady Chlotilde. By the light of the torches Alain saw two whom he recognized. They were envoys of Charlemagne himself. One, with the air of command, was named Hunold, and the other, with the thin, thoughtful face and shaven head, was a churchman, the Bishop Arno.

Alain remembered well the earlier visit these two had made and how his uncle had presented Alain to them.

"This is Alain, who is now my ward, the son of my dead brother," he had said. "But perhaps the name of his mother's brother, Roland, is better known to you, for it is said that Charlemagne called Roland, Count of Brittany, his friend."

Alain remembered how Hunold had put his big fingers under Alain's chin, and turning the boy's face to the light, had looked down at him long and intently. "Yes," he had said at last, "it is many a year since Roland was slain, but those gray eyes are not easily forgotten. Charles, our king, will be glad to hear of him, for he loved Roland well."

Now, even as Alain took his place behind his mother's chair, the Lady Chlotilde spoke. "These noble messengers of the King have brought news that concerns you, Alain," she said.

"Concerns me?" Alain opened his gray eyes wide.

Hunold answered him. "Yes, my boy. Charlemagne, our king, was pleased to learn that you, the nephew of his greatly beloved dead comrade, Roland, had grown to be so likely a lad. He has sent us to bring you back to his palace at Aix."

To Charlemagne, at Aix! Alain's heart gave such a leap that he could hardly get his breath. He looked from Hunold to the bishop and from his uncle to his mother, unable to speak. Suddenly across the table his eye caught that of Bernard. Surprise and envy were plain in Bernard's face. But the bishop had begun to speak, and Alain turned to hear him.

"Our king has become much concerned about the training of the young people in his land," said the bishop. "For this reason he has ordered schools set up for all his subjects, whether nobles or common folk, in the monasteries and in the palaces of the bishops. In his own palace at Aix, he has started a school that will serve as a model. There his own sons and daughters are being taught together with the rest. There you shall go, Alain, to learn to read and to write."

"To read and write!" cried Alain, in astonishment and dismay.

Count Gerhard's broad, healthy face sobered. "Read and write? You had not told me this! Surely the King does not mean to make a clerk of Roland's nephew!"

The whole hall had grown suddenly still. In the silence the fire crackled and a log fell, sending a great tower of sparks up among the rafters overhead.

The bishop continued smoothly, "No, not a clerk, or a churchman, either. But Charles, our king, is wise enough to know that his kingdom will be safer in hands that have skill in other things as well as the sword."

Gerhard shook his head, plainly troubled. "It is not for me to question the King's orders. If he has sent for the boy, go he must. It may be for the best. After all, he's small for his age."

Alain's face grew hot. This was his sorest point — the fact that he was so much smaller than his cousin Bernard. He met Bernard's glance again. There was no envy there now. Even Gisela looked at him with pity in her round blue eyes. With a mumbled excuse, Alain turned and fled into the dark courtyard.

Morning brought bright sunshine, but the boy's heart was still heavy. Charlemagne's orders must be obeyed;

there was no help for that. But to Alain, the King's plan for him seemed a disgrace. Slowly and sadly, he dressed himself for the journey. Because the wind was sharp, he added a sleeveless garment of fur and flung a long blue woolen cloak about his shoulders.

As he stepped into the hall, his mother called to him. "I have something for you, my son," she said. Alain watched eagerly as his mother held out a gold chain, richly carved. On the end of it hung a shining piece of amber. That, too, was carved into a strange and lovely design.

Holding the chain in her hand, the Lady Chlotilde looked earnestly into Alain's face. "I have not spoken much to you of my brother Roland, your uncle," she said. "And the reason is that he was many years older than I, and left our home here in Brittany to serve the King before I can remember. But once, when I was smaller even than Gisela, he returned for a visit before setting forth that last fatal time. I remember well how he picked me up to say good-by. I saw this chain and this amulet gleaming upon his breast, and, as a child will, I caught it in my hands. He took it off and gave it to me.

He said, Keep it, little sister. It has been in our family for many generations. If I were to carry it into so far a country it might be lost. It is said to give good fortune to its wearer if it is worn above a brave, true heart.' Then he kissed me and rode away. And so," said the Lady Chlotilde, holding back the tears that brightened her eyes, "I give it to you, my son, because I know your heart well, and it is both brave and true. And remember — there are other uses for courage besides battle!"

Alain stood very straight while his mother put the chain about his neck. Then together they went out through the great hall, out into the sunshine where the others were already mounted and waiting to be gone. Wearing Roland's chain and amulet, how could his courage fail?

The Power of Words

By noon Alain was farther from home than he had ever been before, even on his longest day of hunting. The forest stretched about them, thick and shadowy. There were no sounds except bird calls, the jingle of harness, and the rattle of the metal plates and rings sewn to the leather jackets of the knights.

They stopped for a lunch of bread and cheese beside a swift little river. Alain noticed that just where the road dipped down to cross the ford there were many great mossy stones lying scattered about as if they had once formed a bridge.

"Yes," said the bishop, when Alain spoke of this. "Doubtless there was a bridge here, for this road that we are traveling was a Roman road, and the Romans were great bridge builders as well as road makers."

"A Roman road?" Alain said. "Do you mean that men from the city of Rome came as far north as this to build roads and bridges?"

The bishop looked at Hunold. "It is high time, indeed, that our king gave thought to schooling," said Arno, "when Imperial Rome is forgotten in the land where Romans lived and worked so long!"

On they rode again, the bishop on a white horse leading the way. Hunold and Alain rode next.

As Alain absently touched his amulet, a thought occurred to him. He turned to Hunold. "You knew my Uncle Roland?" he asked shyly. "Could you tell me about him?"

Hunold's heavy brows drew together as he nodded. "Tell you about him? It was many years ago, but perhaps I can remember." He looked off among the trees as if looking into time long past, and then began his story.

As Alain listened, it seemed to him that the forest melted away from about him. Instead, on either side rose the bare peaks of the Pyrenees. He glanced fearfully up at the trees above him as if they were the rocks that hid Roland's dark-skinned enemies.

More clearly than he saw the bishop, Alain could see Roland on his horse, in golden armor. An ivory horn hung over his shoulder — a horn that he was to blow if attacked. As Hunold told the story, Alain could see Roland going out to fight for his friend, the great Charlemagne. He could see Roland riding into the mountain pass from which he did not return.

"No man knows just what happened there in the pass," said Hunold, "except that Roland was slain. Certainly he never blew upon the ivory horn which would have called warriors to his rescue. Perhaps he did not wish others to risk their lives in order to save his own. Roland was no sturdy giant — he was slight and dark like all Bretons — but he was a great and good knight. And he was gentle, too, and kind. It is sad that such men must be forgotten."

The boy had been so lost in listening that he had not noticed how the forest had begun to thin out. Now he saw with surprise that they were looking out across an open plain, smooth and fertile.

"Ahead lies the monastery where we shall have shelter for the night," said Hunold, pointing to a group of buildings whose thatched roofs showed above the fruit trees.

Inside the walls of the monastery they found a warm welcome. Hot soup, good fresh bread, fish from the river, and fruit from the orchard were served to them on long tables. The stout abbot, anxious to please his important visitors, showed them through the buildings himself.

Alain, following close at the heels of the three men — the abbot, the bishop, and Hunold — listened and looked with all his ears and eyes. At last, in a small room where a western window let in the last of the afternoon light, they found a group of men, young and old, bent over high, slanting desks. They were working busily with feathered quills and ink pots. Bishop Arno paused to pick up the worn yellow parchment from which a young man was copying. "What is this?" he asked.

The abbot peered over his shoulder. "That? It is an old manuscript that we found in the chest of records. It is not from the Scriptures, but our king, as you know, has given orders that all the ancient Latin writings are to be copied as well as the holy words of the saints." He looked anxiously into Arno's face. "I trust it does not displease you that we should preserve this heathen's tale?"

The bishop looked at the manuscript closely for a moment, then put it back on the desk. "I recognize it now. It is part of the writings of the Roman poet, Vergil, telling of the deeds of the great Aeneas. He was a heathen, as you say, but a hero, too. It is written in words which must not be lost. Write well, my son!" He laid a hand kindly on the shoulder of the young man.

297

The men moved on, but Alain remained behind, watching the quill moving so surely, yet so carefully, over the fresh white parchment. "Can you read those words as well as write them?" he asked.

The young man nodded. His eyes, in his thin brown face, glowed. "Copying is work," he said, "but reading — that is the greatest pleasure in life! Standing here with this parchment before me, I can travel miles across seas and lands I never saw, and look upon men and cities now dust for centuries!"

Alain stared at him blankly for a moment. Then his face lighted up as he began to see what the young man meant. "Why, that's the way I felt when Hunold was telling me the story of Roland!" he cried. "Do you mean that all these parchments have stories upon them? That reading is like listening to a tale?"

"Some have stories, some have songs, some have prayers, some have the words of saints or even of Our Lord, some have rules and laws of the land. All are different, but each is like a doorway into a new world!"

"Alain!" called Hunold from outside. "Come, we must find beds for the night. We'll have to be up and away by sunrise."

Obediently Alain followed the old warrior into the fading twilight, his mind whirling with new thoughts. Alone at last in one of the clean, narrow rooms that the monks

kept ready for travelers, he lay down upon the pile of straw in the corner. But he could not sleep. Something tremendous had happened inside his mind. The world seemed changed.

There was nothing dismal, nothing to be ashamed of now in the thought of learning to read and to write. Rather, he looked forward impatiently to the end of his journey. Soon he would be able to read for himself all these brave tales of forgotten days.

As he turned restlessly on his bed of straw, the chain of the amulet slid around his neck and the smooth, cool amber touched his cheek. Then a new idea came to him, so dazzling that he lay perfectly still, while the rising moon shone through the narrow window and threw leaf-shadows on the white wall above his head. Perhaps he, Alain, could write out the story of Roland some day, just the way Hunold had told it to him there in the dark forest, his words timed to the steady beat of their horses' hoofs! Then, like the song of Aeneas, it would not be forgotten when those who had known Roland were dead and gone. The name of Roland would stand forever in men's minds, a symbol of gallant courage and unfailing loyalty!

There was a smile on Alain's face as he fell asleep.

Margaret Leighton

THE MIGHT OF A SONG

WHO WILL RESCUE RICHARD?

RICHARD is captured! Richard is captured!"
The news began as a whisper, no louder than a light breeze. It traveled from peasant to squire, from squire to knight, from page to lady, from village to town, from castle to castle, from land to land.

"Did you hear the news? Richard the Lion-Hearted, on his way home from the Crusade, has been captured by Leopold of Austria and put in prison."

"Where?"

"Who knows?"

"In which prison?"

"Who can say?"

The whisper grew to a shout. For all Richard's enemies it was a shout of joy: for John of England, Richard's brother, who might now seize the throne; for Philip of France, who planned now to seize Normandy; for Leopold of Austria, who hid his royal prisoner well.

For others the shout ended in a groan: for Richard's knights-at-arms; for his mother, Queen Eleanor of Aquitaine; for the troubadours, those wandering poets and singers of songs, especially Blondel, who dearly loved him; for Blondel's apprentice, Raimon, who loved both Blondel and the King.

In a castle in Normandy, Blondel and his five apprentices were spending a fortnight. They were singing of the Crusade to the Lady Fleurande, whose lord was off on a hunt.

As they sang, who should enter the courtyard but Jacques the tinker, with his pots and pans on his back, and the news on his tongue — "Richard is in prison — somewhere in Austria."

"You jest!" Blondel and his lads, with the folk of the castle, swarmed about Jacques like bees to a comb. "Do you swear it?"

"My life upon it," cried tinker Jacques. "I had it of honest Robert, and Robert of honest Pierre. . . ."

Then Blondel begged for his tale.

So Jacques told of how a storm blew Richard's ship from its course as he sailed home from the Crusade, and wrecked him on the shores of the Adriatic Sea. From there Richard and his page made their way disguised as merchants to the city of Vienna — to the very home of his enemy, Leopold of Austria. Then, in the market, his page boasted of his master with too loose a tongue, so that the secret came out. When it reached the Duke's ears, he sent armed men to the inn where Richard slept. They found under the coat of a merchant the heart of a lion.

Yet for all the blows Richard struck out at the guard, they took him at last. They hid him away, no man knew where.

"Now, by St. Julian," Blondel cried, as he struck a loud chord on his lute, "that is the sorriest, saddest tale ever man told. Come," he called to his five apprentices. "Come, let us away. We must see what is to be done."

And they all took fair and courteous leave of the Lady Fleurande. When she begged Blondel to stay on, he said he must go, for with Richard in danger, he must try to help him.

Raimon, alone of the five apprentices, pressed closer to ask, "Where shall we look for our King, my master?"

"We go first to the castle of Sir Bertran de Born," Blondel replied. "He will know how to free the King."

Now it chanced that they were the first to bring the sad news. And once it was told in the great hall, the whole castle soon gathered about them.

The old warrior Bertran de Born swore a great oath. "God's curse upon Duke Leopold! Let me ride at him till his teeth fall from his head at the shock; till the secret be forced from his lips."

And knight Bertran, who loved nothing so much on this earth as a fight, stamped the length of the hall till you would think a herd of wild boars had passed by.

"Once I have learned where Richard is held, there will I ride my horse Bayard. I, who have broken a thousand spears, will hurl my battle-ax over the wall. Let me but find Leopold of Austria and he shall feel the cut of my sword."

Blondel let him storm. He dropped his head in his hands as he sat by the fire. Words were fierce things, but easy to speak. To lay siege to a royal castle was not child's play, no, nor the work of one man. And Blondel saw in his mind's eye the map of Europe. He looked at the lands between the seas — from the Adriatic to the North Sea and the Baltic. In his mind he spread out the lands: the mountains and valleys, rivers and plains, with a castle on every crag. Blondel lifted his head from his hands.

The old knight stormed on. "Not by lying in prison will Richard conquer his enemies and regain the thrones of England and Aquitaine. By Our Lady, I must gather my men. We'll not wait to know where he lies. We must fight a glorious fight. Our enemies will fall thick and fast. Tents and castles will be destroyed. Then Richard shall go free."

"Gently, gently, my brother," Blondel smiled. Such a mad storming of castles would take money — money and men. And, as he knew only too well, Bertran's money was spent. Not a war in the land these many long years but he had fought in it. He had come home from the Crusade a poor man.

Besides, who now would help him fight for Richard the Lion-Hearted? Many knights now would rejoice over his imprisonment.

But Blondel's own apprentices shared Bertran's fierce threats. They liked well to imagine themselves starting off to battle. So now they marched behind Bertran up and down the long hall, blowing their horns.

Blondel smiled. He was fond of his apprentices, but fondest of Raimon, youngest of them all. Raimon's head was thrown back, his blue eyes shining with light, as he went marching and strumming and singing a war song.

Yet Blondel knew it would take more than force to free the young king. Someone must find him first. Blondel could see that well enough, now. He thought how the guild of troubadours were to meet in Paris this month. Who but the troubadours could cook up a plan?

So off they went to Paris, Blondel the troubadour and his five apprentice lads.

In and out of castles, in and out of inns, they traveled, singing the story of Richard's great deeds, singing the third Crusade. And as they traveled, they listened to the buzzing of tongues, listened for the secret that somebody knew, the secret of where Richard lay in some unknown prison.

So they came to the gates of Paris itself. Most men paid an entrance fee, but not these travelers. By the troubadours' law, Blondel and his group sang and strummed, piped and blew their way through the gate, without fee. They made their way to the quarter east of the Cathedral of Our Lady, Notre Dame de Paris.

Here they found themselves among friends. From north and south, from east and west, troubadours and their apprentices gathered here, till the narrow lanes swarmed with them. Surely, here they would find news. For who had not heard the sorry tale? It buzzed on all men's tongues. It leaped forth from all men's songs. Where was Richard hid? In which of the many Austrian prisons? Who could say? Who could tell?

"This is a matter for knights," the northern troubadours said.

The knights shook their helmeted heads.

"This is a matter for kings," they said.

The kings shook their crowned heads.

"This is a matter for the Church," they said.

Yet the monks shook their heads, too.

"This is the business of everybody here," cried the monks.

"Then if it is everybody's business, it is nobody's," said Blondel, "but at least it shall be my business." His words rang out like a challenge.

"Ho, my lads," he blew on his horn.

The apprentices came running. "What is it, Master?"

Blondel drew them away from the crowd, to the church of St. Julian, patron saint of troubadours.

"Now, by our patron saint, lads, I have decided to go forth alone in search of our king. Surely a song is mightier than a sword to storm castle walls. But I must travel fast and hard. I can take but one of you with me. Which shall it be?"

"Take me, my Master."

"Take me."

"No, no, take me."

All five begged at once. They looked at Blondel with shining, eager eyes.

"What now! Would you be willing to start at the beginning of winter?"

Their faces fell. Winter was the time for staying within their own castle. When the north wind howled without and the sleet blew into men's faces, when the roads were knee-deep in mud, and the snow piled to the eaves, then apprentices hugged the warm fire. Then they learned the new songs which their masters, the troubadours, composed. All day they dozed and sang, or tossed balls and caught naked knives in their hands. All day they laughed at the wind and snapped their fingers at the cold.

As Blondel looked at his apprentices now, he read their thoughts. "Tell me, lads, just what would you do now for your king? How would you spend the long winter months?"

"I'd learn a new ballad as would touch all men's hearts in the spring," the first apprentice said.

"I'd practice with the sword in our own courtyard, Master," said the second, "and so be ready to fight."

"Aye, so would we all," agreed the third and fourth.

Blondel turned to Raimon. "And you, lad?"

"I'd walk to land's end for him, my Master, through mud or through snow. I'd storm every castle of Austria, not with sword, but with song." Thus spoke the young Raimon, youngest of them all.

Blondel's eyes glowed as if a fire had been lighted within. He turned to the four. "Go now back to Sir Bertran, lads," he said. "Say to him that Blondel sent you to his school of the sword. When Richard is found, I'll return. For this difficult search, I need take only Raimon with me."

So the four apprentices, thinking their master as mad as a hare, went back to make merry in the streets of Paris.

Blondel's Vow

Blondel drew Raimon with him inside the church of St. Julian. While his master prayed, Raimon looked about him. The thick stone walls shut out every sound from outside. Here all was still. Tiny candle flames lighted the altar before which Blondel knelt. St. Julian, patron saint of troubadours, looked down from the painted windows.

Raimon's eyes came back from the windows to his master. Blondel rose, lighted two candles, and gave one to the boy. Quickly Raimon crossed himself and knelt beside Blondel at the altar to Our Lady.

"Now, by Our Lady and her knight Julian," prayed Blondel earnestly, "we two humble singers of songs do set forth to find our lord, King Richard. Go with us, blessed patron saint, and keep us from all dangers, that we may speedily accomplish our purpose."

"Amen," murmured Raimon, "and amen."

He saw Blondel lift from his shoulder the blue ribbon of his favorite lute. He saw Blondel step inside the marble rail and hang the lute over the shoulder of the blue-robed Virgin Mary.

"Wear it for me, my Lady, for I vow never again to touch its strings till Richard is found."

Raimon's eyes shone. "He means that from now on, I am to play for him while he sings," he thought.

"Give us now a sign of thy grace," Blondel begged.

Suddenly, out of the stillness, they heard a low chord, as if gentle fingers wandered over the strings of Blondel's lute. Startled, Raimon and Blondel looked up, and stared into each other's eyes.

Surely it was the sign Blondel had prayed for! Surely it was the Lady of Heaven whose white fingers had struck that low chord on Blondel's lute!

Dazed with wonder and joy, they stumbled to their feet and tiptoed out through the heavy oaken door.

On the porch, Blondel took Raimon in his arms, and kissed the boy on both cheeks.

"Let this be our secret, lad," he whispered. "Surely it was a sign that our search will not be in vain. Come, let us be off."

Blondel mounted his horse, Valiant. Raimon walked behind. Thus they set out on their search for the prison in which Richard the Lion-Hearted was held.

The rains came. The cold wind blew on their backs and whistled down their necks. The roads were deep with mud. Often enough Raimon shivered to his very bones. The snow fell. It might be pretty to see, but it was cold and wet to feel. It was difficult to keep the instruments dry, hung over his shoulders in their leather cases. But steadily he plodded on behind Blondel's horse.

They crossed France, they crossed Germany, they crossed Bohemia, and came at last to Vienna in Austria. Still there was no news of their king.

"Do all the roads go uphill?" Raimon asked.

"Yes," Blondel answered. For every Austrian castle sat on a crag, every prison on the very crest of a hill. With so many robbers in the land, a man was never a king except within his own castle walls.

Ever they pressed on, asking cautiously in each town, "Are there prisoners, perhaps, in the near-by castle?" But never did they hear of one who might be Richard.

So the months wore on. Christmas and New Year's and St. Patrick's days sped by and it was almost Easter. Still the two kept on.

One glad spring day, Raimon stood stretching his neck to look at the castle called Durenstein on a mountain of rock above the Danube.

"Only an eagle would have chosen that crag, Master," he said.

Blondel nodded. He, too, was staring up at the flag flying from the highest tower. It bore a two-headed black eagle — Leopold's own flag!

He frowned, as he pulled up his horse's head.

For, that morning, Valiant had gone lame. Though Raimon drew out the stone, still he limped. The truth was, the horse was as weary as his master, as weary as his master's apprentice, whose clothes were tattered and torn. Blondel's coat, too, was shabby. They did not stay long enough in one castle to earn a new coat. Yet he turned with a smile to the lad leaning against the barred gate across the path up the castle hill.

"Up, lad, and over the gate. Announce our coming, and pray the lord courteously for his good cheer. And keep sharp ears and a sharper wit in your head."

Raimon squared his shoulders, where the straps of his instruments bit deep. He forced his lips to smile.

"Stay here in the shelter of this tree, Master, and let poor Valiant rest his foot. No doubt, the lord will send a fresh horse for you."

Blondel nodded. "You have a brave heart and a sweet tongue, lad. I shall ask Richard one day to make you his troubadour."

Neither would admit defeat, nor hunger, nor poverty. So Blondel got stiffly down from his horse, and Raimon leaped over the gate to begin his long climb.

313

The path was steep and the stones cut Raimon's feet. Since the winter storms, the stones that had been washed down from above still lay where they fell. Clearly the lord and his men were from home. Neither men nor beasts had come this way since winter. Surely, then, the castle must be deserted, for all its fluttering flag.

"No need to climb more," said his legs.

"Stop and rest here," said his feet.

"Both you and Master are too tired now to sing," said his throat.

"Come, stop, Master, let us rest," legs, feet, and throat all cried out together as with one voice. "Use your head. What's it for? Reason it out. Without a lord there are no men, and without men there could be no prisoners — certainly no such prisoner as Richard."

Raimon stared up at the tower. He listened. There was no sound of man or beast above the chirping of birds.

"Well, then, have it your way," he said crossly, and he caught up two blades of grass, a short and a long, and shut them into his fist so that only the tops might show. "Which shall it be? Let the short blade say 'stay' and the long blade say 'go.'"

Raimon pulled. It was the long blade he drew.

"You see for yourself," he said to his tired legs and feet, "now we've got to keep on. Even if we drop in our tracks, the King must be found."

So he set off up the hill, and as he went, he whistled a tune — panted and whistled. Around the next curve he came to a stop. In a cleared space sat a girl and her geese.

The girl started up and her cheeks flushed bright pink. The geese fluttered their wings and scolded him in loud hisses. From above he heard the sudden barking of dogs. He looked at the girl and bowed low as if to a princess, a long sweeping bow with his hand on his heart. It was not hard to remember his manners, for the girl was very fair, with eyes the blue of her long gown. On her hair was a wreath she had woven of spring flowers.

As Raimon stared at her he wished his clothes were not so tattered or his hair so rumpled. Then he remembered his errand.

"Tell me, fair maid, who lives in this castle?" He spoke in the Austrian tongue.

"The castle is Duke Leopold's," she answered, "but my lord has not been home for a year."

"Just as I thought," said Raimon. "I might better have saved both my legs and my breath."

"Saved them? For what? For whom?"

Raimon laughed. "For castles whose dukes stay at home to guard their prisoners," he nodded across to the next hill, "like that one over there, perhaps? Surely there are prisoners there."

"I doubt it, sir. The Lady Marguerite is far too kind-hearted for that."

Raimon sighed. She was smiling at him, looking hard at his lute. She came a step closer and pointed to it.

"Tell me, sweet sir, would you sing me one song?"

"My throat is so dry it would croak like a frog in a dry pond."

At their sudden laughter together, the geese honked, and the dogs above barked fiercely. Raimon looked up in alarm.

316

"Don't mind them," the girl said. "They are only our stout men-at-arms to keep away strangers who might prowl about the castle at night."

"Oh, I see," said Raimon a little breathlessly. "Then tell me, what is your name?"

She smiled at him. "Marie is my name, kind sir."

"Oh, you were named for Our Lady."

"Yes." She reached out her hand to the lute. "I do so love music. If only you would sing!" She touched the strings, a gentle touch that made a light chord.

Raimon looked at her with startled eyes. "That is the sign — Her sign, and your name is Marie!"

Her blue eyes widened.

"Then listen to me, little Marie, and I shall sing you a song." He closed his eyes and swept his fingers across the strings. He sang in French:

> "Your eyes are blue as waving flax,
> And your cheeks are as pink as a rose."

The tune was that of a little French song, but the words he made up as he sang.

Marie clapped her hands. "But that is the same tune the prisoner sings!"

"The prisoner! You mean, you have prisoners there?"

"Only one," she protested, "and often I hear him singing French songs." She clapped her hand over her

317

mouth, and, gathering up her long blue dress, she ran from him. Up the hill path she went, calling her geese to follow.

With three strides, Raimon had caught up with her and barred the path.

"Listen to me, Marie. Go up there and tell your mother that she shall have the honor of sheltering this night a famous troubadour — that's my master — and his apprentice, Raimon. You shall have songs and more songs, all the songs you most wish to hear. My heart is full of them. And tell her to chain up the dogs, and ask the hens to lay us an egg."

As Marie started up the path, driving her geese before her, Raimon was off down the hill. His feet had grown wings. Surely, the sign of Our Lady could not fail! Surely, this time they had found the prisoner they sought!

An hour later, Raimon and his master wandered about the courtyard. In a corner they saw the prison, its narrow windows barred with iron. Within, it must be black as night.

Marie's mother hurried about, getting supper. The castle was a lonely place with the lord and court all from home, and she was delighted to hear the gossip of the wide world. So Raimon strummed his lute, and Blondel sang of the Crusades and of the countries through which they had traveled. Out of courtesy to their hostess, they sang in the Austrian tongue.

After supper they wandered again about the courtyard, this time close under the prison window, while Raimon strummed. At a nod from his master, Raimon broke into the tune which he had sung for Marie that afternoon. Blondel sang the first verse. They paused and listened, waiting and hoping. All was still within the prison.

Blondel turned away, weary and discouraged.

"Once more! Try once more!" whispered Raimon forcefully.

Again Blondel sang the first verse of the song, somewhat louder than before. Hark! From within the prison came a voice, singing the second verse of that very song which Blondel and King Richard had composed together.

"Now praise be unto God and Our Lady," Blondel chanted joyously in the Latin tongue, "for that our search is ended, and Blondel and Raimon may return home."

And out of the prison came a hearty "Amen, and Amen. The mighty shall fall from their thrones, but the little ones shall be lifted to the stars."

Then Raimon could not help composing a song of his own, about how the blessed Virgin had sent them a sign, a chord on a lute, a song that was mightier than a sword.

All that evening Blondel sang wonderful songs and Raimon played merry tunes till the feet of all in the castle fell to dancing.

With the dawn, they bade a courteous farewell to the little maid, Marie, and her mother and sped away down the steep hill. As fast as they could travel along the spring roads, they hurried to tell the English Court that Richard was found. Now his friends could gather gold with which to pay for his release.

Eloise Lownsbery

MARCO POLO

NOTHING much had happened in Venice for some time, and people had almost ceased to ask one another, "What's the news?" Then, on a fine day in 1269, there was enough and to spare to talk about. Fifteen-year-old Marco Polo, a bright-eyed and straight-limbed lad, had more to tell than anyone.

On that fine day three men who turned out to be brothers knocked at the Polo door. They told the porter who opened it that they owned the house, though people who lived in it did not know them. They were tanned, bearded, dressed in travel-worn clothes, but they soon proved that they had money to spend.

One of them, whose eyes glistened as he spoke, laid a gentle hand on Marco's shoulder. Then, looking straight into the lad's face, he said, "So you are my son, are you? I'm proud of you." Explanations followed.

While he listened, Marco remembered what his mother had told him a few months before she died: that his father had gone to far-off lands just before Marco was born, to a place called Cathay, where few travelers had ever gone. There had been no news of his father in all these years.

When Marco compared what he remembered with what the three men said, things fitted together. He came to know that his father's name was Nicolo, and that he was something of an engineer as well as a trader. One uncle, Matteo, had traveled with Nicolo. The other had been a trader in Constantinople, doing a good business, and would return there soon.

Then it came out that Marco's father and the uncle who had been to China were no common travelers, but had been received by rulers and great folk. They spoke strange languages and liked China very much indeed, and the Chinese, too. They even thought Europe was backward by comparison. Far from being content at home, they intended to return, taking a hundred learned men with them. They had promised the Grand Khan to do so, and honor demanded that promises should be kept.

322

When it came out that they would return to China, there was small need for them to say to Marco Polo, "Come with us." His heart, indeed, was set on the adventure. For the vast unknown has called to men since the world began.

What Marco Polo Saw

What with one thing and another, two years passed before Marco, his father Nicolo, and his uncle Matteo were ready to go on their way. But instead of a hundred learned men, they had been able to persuade only two monks to go with them. Even those two lost heart very early on the journey and turned back home.

Father Nicolo and Uncle Matteo and seventeen-year-old Marco were made of sterner stuff and there was no drawing back for them. On they went across plain and over mountain, one day feasting and another fasting with good grace. As they overcame difficulties, they became stronger until, in a desert, the lad Marco came down with fever and lay for a while between life and death. It took a year in the highlands of what is now Afghanistan to set him on his feet again, but it was by no means an idle year. During that time they made many excursions, found out a great deal about the people and their ways, and, like good travelers, learned a new language.

Then on the Polos went, sometimes among people who gave them a free and fair welcome, and at other times among less kindly folk. They traveled over highest mountains, across deserts, along ancient roads, often thirsty and often tightening their belts to stay the pangs of hunger, always stout of heart. Sometimes they rested for weeks among friendly folk but sometimes they traveled long and late to make good speed. So, in the year 1275, they came to the Khan's court and were well received.

The scene stayed in Marco Polo's mind. There was the Khan on his throne with attendants in gorgeous dress. There were the ruler's sons, grandsons, and relatives on lower seats. There were the musicians, attendants, and visiting lords bearing gifts. And among that glittering crowd stood the three Polos, travel-stained but assured, and received by the Grand Khan with all honors.

In after years, while he was in prison and China seemed to him a very desirable place, Marco Polo described the scene at length. In all, he spent seventeen years in China but his first impressions never faded. It seemed to him that Europe was in a barbaric state compared with that country. China was peaceful; Europe was war torn. In Europe, the roads were mostly ruts made by cartwheels. In towns, garbage and other refuse were thrown into the streets to decay so that fires had to be lighted occasionally to "purify the air." There were public pillories, hangings, and torturings for small offenses. There were also Black Plagues and Peasant Revolts.

In Europe, printing was still unknown and would not be known for another hundred years, although it was already an ancient art in China. In China, he had seen towns "disposed in squares," with guards patrolling the streets. He had seen parks with fountains, and tree-shaded highways, and noble bridges.

Venice, in those days, knew nothing of coal. In China, he had seen people dig "a sort of black stone out of the mountains" . . . a stone which held the heat much better than wood. He had seen, too, the people of Cathay make use of "a fountain of oil," using it for lighting. He had wondered at asbestos cloth, of which his native Venice would know nothing for two hundred years.

At one of the ports, he saw the river crowded with rich ships full of merchandise coming from India. The town of Kin-sai was beautiful with paved ways and arched drains. In the Province of Manji, the people were so well provided for and so wisely governed that "when shops, filled with goods" were "left open, no person entered to rob them of the smallest article" and "travelers might pass through every part of the kingdom by night as well as by day, freely, without danger."

There was the wonder of people using paper money which was received as gladly as gold and silver. There were inns or post-houses throughout the land, finely furnished; and he had seen a mail service by pony express which ran regularly. He had wondered and admired when he learned that every year the Grand Khan sent forth inspectors to see if drought or storm had ruined any poor people's crops. When such was the case, those people were freed from taxes until better times, and supplied with grain, that none might go hungry.

Marco Polo had seen canals in his travels. He had also watched road inspectors seeing to it that road repairs were made promptly. He was especially interested in a certain stone bridge five hundred yards long and wide enough for ten horsemen to ride side by side. He had seen water clocks, fire companies, street cleaners, public baths, playgrounds for children, none of which were to be found in Europe. And, like a good traveler, Marco remembered what he saw and was persuaded that China was civilized while Europe was still half-barbaric.

Envoy of the Grand Khan

It is very clear, then, that Marco Polo was one of those who went about wide awake, who took an intelligent interest in the world about him. It is also well known that every ruler of men, every honest man in high office, is looking for young people with such qualities.

326

The Grand Khan, whose territory covered half of the known world, was no exception. Also there was proof enough that Marco Polo was persistent, else he would

never have made that journey. So there was the ruler, and there was the kind of young man he wanted. To make everything fit in place, a job appeared.

The Khan wanted to know how matters were going in the distant province of Yunen, and Marco Polo seemed to be the right sort to send. So Marco Polo went as the Khan's envoy. He saw with a fresh and eager eye and took care that he was not swayed by prejudice. Then, the work done, he told his story with proper sparkle, to the Khan's delight. His report did not limit itself to taxation alone. No, indeed, he went into matters more deeply, showing trade possibilities in the province. He reported on the manners and customs of the people, their food and their way of cooking. He had made notes of what was grown, of distances between places, and even the tricks that traders played.

Marco Polo's manner was exact. When he knew a thing surely he came out with a "This is so" or "I know because I saw." When he did not see with his own eyes, he took care to say "I was told" or "They say." He did not repeat a rumor without branding it as rumor, a habit that pleased his master, the Khan, very greatly.

Marco Polo's visit to the distant territory of Basman was an interesting example of his habit of looking into things. The report ran that a race of very small dwarfs lived there, and the tale seemed to be confirmed because people from Basman had shown what they said were mummified bodies of members of this race. Naturally Marco Polo had to look into the matter, and his discoveries put an end to the dwarf trade. For he found that there were, in that district, monkeys with wrinkled faces that looked almost human. The native traders caught these monkeys, and killed and shaved them. Next they dried the bodies, arranged the limbs to look like those of human beings, perfumed the bodies with camphor, and put them in boxes to be sold to strangers.

We can imagine the Khan hearing Marco Polo's tale with high interest, an interest which certainly did not lessen when Marco went on to tell how the people of Basman declared their loyalty to the Khan but paid him no taxes at all. They felt safe in their position because they were far from the capital, and the road was so rough that tax collectors were not likely to travel their way.

Of such important nature were Marco's reports: always exact, interesting, just, and fair. By them, the Khan came to know a great deal about the provinces over which he ruled. And as envoy, Marco traveled far and wide, to Cochin-China, to India, to Burma, to Japan. Then came promotion. The Khan gave him the position of governor of Yang Chow, a province where war munitions were made, and troops were stationed. Marco Polo was treated like a prince in Yang Chow and ruled there for three years.

THE RETURN OF THE POLOS

Meanwhile, Marco's father and uncle had positions of
trust which paid well. Also they were clever traders, so
that the time came when the three Polos counted themselves rich and began to think of Venice as a place in which
to end their days. But, when they talked of leaving, the
Khan frowned on the idea. Then, by great good luck,
something happened to solve their problem.

The ruler of Persia, who had set his mind on marrying
a beautiful princess in the Khan's court, sent an envoy to
escort the lady, who was seventeen years old, to Persia.
But there were wars in Tartary so that the Persian envoys
did not want to take the risk of travel across the war-torn

country with a princess to guard. To go by sea seemed better, they told the Khan, if he would permit the three Polos, who were used to the sea, to sail with them. To this plan the liberal-minded Khan agreed. What was more, he gave orders that the Polo possessions should be turned into jewels and precious stones, as easier to carry. Also he saw to it that they should travel grandly.

So, in the year 1292, the Polos sailed out of port with a fleet of ships, bound for Venice by way of Persia. But what with storms and contrary winds, delays and difficulties, it was two years before the voyage ended, and it cost the lives of six hundred men. As for the princess, when she reached Persia she was told that her bridegroom had died, but that one of his sons by an early marriage was also looking for a wife. So the beautiful princess married the son and did not have her journey for nothing.

The three Polos were equally fortunate, for the prince, or one of his men, saw to it that they were provided with horses and guards for their journey by land through Persia. Thus they came safely enough to Venice in the year 1295.

The story runs that the three travelers had trouble persuading the people of Venice that they were, indeed, the Polos who had gone to Cathay twenty-four years earlier. But when they showed jewels and precious stones, silks and satins, and many a rare treasure, the doubters believed.

Probably the return of the Polos was no more than a

nine days' wonder, for there were other excitements to engage men's attention. Venice was at war with Genoa, and Marco could not stay quiet when there were lively times abroad. So he became commander of a galley, was captured in the battle of Curzola on September 7, 1296, and was imprisoned in Genoa for three years.

Perhaps, if it had not been for that imprisonment, the world would never have learned Marco Polo's story, for, as the poet Pindar said, "Many great deeds are lost in darkness for lack of song." One of Marco Polo's fellow-prisoners, having heard something of the tale, persuaded the traveler to dictate it to him. This Marco did in very bad French. So when he was released, and returned to Venice in 1299, he had with him the manuscript of his book, "The Travels of Marco Polo."

An old saying runs, "A traveler hath leave to lie," and for many years in his own land Marco Polo was considered just a teller of tales. Indeed, on the occasion of pageants and plays, a comic character acting the part of "Marco Polo, the Million Man," often appeared on the stage. But from the reports of later travelers, we know that Marco Polo, in his story, stuck close to truth.

Charles J. Finger

TOM PEAR–TREE

TOM GAINSBOROUGH did not like school when he had sums or spelling to do. But he never had any trouble with writing. Any copy set him was done skillfully and exactly. But he was always more anxious to go sketching in the forest than to do his lessons.

"Father," he said one night at the supper table, "will you send the schoolmaster a note tomorrow, saying I am to have a holiday?"

His father, a busy manufacturer of woolen goods in Sudbury, England, looked up from his plate.

"I should rather say not, Tom," he answered firmly. "Attend school at the proper time and don't idle. What would your master say?"

Young Tom went to bed, disappointed. As he was one of nine children and shared a room with his brothers, he had to wait until the others were asleep to plan a piece of mischief. Then he got up. Carefully and as neatly as possible, he wrote on a piece of paper, "Give Tom a holiday," and took it to school the next day.

The English schoolmaster, who had many boys under his charge in this year of 1737, would certainly have punished Tom had he known the trick that was being played upon him. But he was busy and it would be a relief to have one lively boy the less in class. So he growled out, thinking the note was from Tom's father, "If your father asks it, I suppose you must go."

The truant went to the woods as he had planned. He was not a bad boy, just gay, light-hearted, and wrapped up in his drawing and painting.

His busy mother painted flowers well and had given him his first sketching lessons. She took a great interest in his work, but his father did not. It was Tom's dearest wish to leave the grammar school and be apprenticed to an artist. But his father would not grant the wish, though he was devoted to the boy.

Today was not the first time Tom had wandered deep into the Suffolk woods and the near-by pastures where sheep grazed and doves flew over his head. Like another boy from Stratford-on-Avon, two hundred years before, he was always running away, always plunging into the forest. He was perfectly happy alone. "I do believe," he said to himself, "that I know every single tree, hedge, and stump about here by heart."

Tom Gainsborough did not idle in the woods. How he loved the shadows! His pencil flew all day sketching and setting down the charming scenes he saw. His brothers and sisters would not have cared for them, but to him they were enough. When he came out of the woods at twilight,

334

he came upon a cottage where some ragged children were
playing. They looked poor. He was feeling gay and
light-hearted because of his adventure and wanted to do
something for someone. So he gave them the two or three
pennies he had in his pockets.

This day of stolen freedom was never discovered by the
teacher.

On another day, Tom was hiding among the thick
currant and gooseberry bushes on the edge of his father's
orchard. Here stood an old pear tree loaded with pears,
fresh and wet with dew. The pear tree was like a person
to young Tom; he could have given it a name.

Deep in his sketching, he suddenly noticed a face — the face of another human being who did not see him. This man was leaning far over the wall. His greedy eyes were on those ripe pears. His half-open mouth was watering for them. As he reached out his hand to pick the nearest one, Tom caught the likeness perfectly and sketched it on his paper.

Then, making a move among the bushes, he startled the man, who took to his heels and disappeared. Tom carried the sketch he had made to his father, who had just returned home.

"Well, I say!" The older man studied it in amazement. "If that isn't the image of Dick Goding, who's always taking fruit out of my orchard! Where did you see him, boy?"

In fact, Father Gainsborough was so much amused that he sent for Dick Goding and teased him well by saying, "You were planning to shake down my pears and fill your stomach with them before I did. See, now, my boy caught you in the very act. I know what you intended to do. Look at this picture!"

The man stared at the picture. He could not speak. He swallowed, choked, and gasped with confusion. The owner of the orchard laughed good-naturedly and let him go, with a warning to leave other people's fruit alone in the future.

336

That night Gainsborough made a decision. Calling young Tom to him, he said, "Tom, I'm going to apprentice you to a silversmith. If you can catch a likeness as skillfully as you did Dick's, you must use what gifts you have." He watched his son's face light up as he uttered the magic words.

Through the silversmith Tom soon entered an art school and began to study painting in earnest. One day he was to be famous for his "landskips," as he called them, as well as for his portraits. That orchard back of the Black Horse Inn at Sudbury was always shown as the spot where his first real portrait was made. The sketch of Dick Goding was called "Tom Pear-Tree" and copied on wood cut into the figure of a man.

In Tom's own mind, his landscapes were always his best work. What he had felt and seen on his many happy days in the forest went into them — the solitary quiet, the grazing animals, the great overhanging trees, the lengthening shadows. What Tom Gainsborough loved in the countryside was the heart of his home — England — and he made other people feel and care for it as he did.

Laura Benét

WITH A BARBER'S BRUSH

W HAT a fog! A boy dressed in rough clothes and weighted with the names of Joseph Mallord William Turner looked sadly out of a window one cold April day in 1786. Maiden Lane, in the poor quarter of East London, was wrapped in a fog, filled with the smoke of many stoves. It was as if someone had hung a heavy blanket over the city of London.

The boy's bright blue eyes watched the dismal scene. He felt, high up in the old house, as if he were alone on an island. Only the barking of dogs and the footsteps of tradespeople walking cautiously along to avoid accidents

338

gave signs of life in the ugly, dirty street. Even in the barber shop on the ground floor where William's jolly, clever little father carried on his trade of barber, there were no voices. This lack of customers would upset William Turner, Senior, who had a keen eye for business. He had not much time to give his son but he was kind-hearted and honest, and had taught William to be saving even of halfpennies.

Ever since William's mother died, he and his father had kept house together over the barber shop. It was William who washed the windows and swept the sidewalk, ran to the fishmarket and the butcher's, and did their bit of cooking. The boy was small, sturdy, and sunny-tempered, so that all these things were done willingly. He and his father were good companions.

In his free time William had great fun. He was fond of sports. The barber shop, the center of his world, was only five minutes from the Thames River, where he played exciting games with other boys under London Bridge. Best of all, he liked making friends with the sailors. They would take him for rides on barges up and down the river. Those blue eyes of his watched life on the water and sparkled with delight over clouds and sunsets. After looking carefully at a ship, he could come home and draw it.

On this foggy day in April, William had planned great

adventures and was angry at the weather for spoiling his schemes. But he would do something else. He would get very busy at his favorite indoor amusement — painting. He would bring color, rich color, into this gray foggy day. He would put down on a square of paper something that glowed even through a mist.

Dragging a table over to the window to catch what light there was, he found there was not enough to paint by. So, at the risk of what his father called waste, he lighted two candles and placed them on the table. His head was full of things to paint. He often made sketches of the other boys at his school, and, in return, they helped William with his sums. Even his schoolmaster noticed the drawings. Some pictures he had made of birds and trees were hung on the schoolroom wall. But now he would do even better.

The two candles burned brightly. That was fine, and helped him immensely. Next he searched for his paints and an old rag in a cupboard. Where two men, one middle-aged, one young, lived together, there was not much order, but he found his precious paints, and next, his brush. Oh, what was this? All he held in his hand was a brush handle. The mouse who so often visited the cupboard had found no crumb of cheese, no bit of candle to nibble, and so he had devoted himself to gnawing the bristles of William's one paint brush! The boy wondered what he could do.

He had no wish to lose himself in the fog, as would surely happen if he ran to the shop some distance away to buy a new brush.

Suddenly his eye lighted with a merry look. He would try an experiment. The tall old house had steep stairs. Down, down he stole and peered through the open door of the barber shop. Empty! His father had put on his coat and gone out, probably to the house of some rich man to dress his hair; or to bleed someone, for barbers were doctors as well, in the eighteenth century.

William went over to the stand where his father kept the shaving brushes. They were clean, washed free of soap. Why couldn't he paint a picture with one of these? He would — and explain about it later. The poor barber's best brush was chosen. It answered William's purpose well.

In his nook by a window on the second floor, young William Turner bent his head, almost touching his long nose to the paper, as he began his picture. His subject was a sunset over the Thames in the bright colors he loved — strong reds and light blues and pale yellows. He worked without stopping for several hours. There was not a sound in the room except coal dropping from the neglected fire in the grate and the house cat moving about. Sometimes she leaped on his shoulder to have a look at his work. At last he heard his father's step on the stairs, his hand on the door. The water color was done! Wiping the barber brush hastily with a rag he ran down to the shop by a back flight of stairs and put it back on the stand.

When he reached their rooms again, he found his father blowing the fire. "You were right to be careful about the coals, boy," said the little man, turning around. "But why did you light two candles? Waste, waste," he went on, scolding, yet good-natured, as he quickly snuffed out one with his thumb and finger. "You were making a picture, I suppose."

"Yes, Father, I was. Here it is."

The barber came and stood by the table. He nodded his head. "You should show that picture to the schoolmaster. It makes a grand bit of color." He looked proudly at his son. "I sold another of your sketches today," he went on. "One of those I hung up on the shop wall along with the wigs. I got ninepence for it. Here is the money. Dear me, dear me, trade was terrible today. I'll be ruined entirely if these fogs keep up. Have you fried the fish?"

"No, not yet. But I will."

William's hands were quick, and it was not long before the two friends, father and son, sat down to their supper of fish, bread, and cheese. There was no pudding tonight.

More than once William was on the point of telling his father that he had used the brush. But he saw that his father was tired.

"Only people who can afford a coach and horses," his father sighed, "can get about on such foggy nights. I was run into more than once coming back from curling Lord Haviland's hair."

The next morning was clear, for a high wind had blown away the last of the dread fog. William got off to school with a light heart. The older William Turner's spirits went up, too. Hardly had the shutters of the shop been taken down when a customer arrived, one who came often. He was a pompous man with a heavy beard on his chin, who badly needed a shave.

Turner seated him in the chair and mixed the soap. Then, taking up the same brush that had painted his son's fine sunset, he began to lather the older man's face. All at once, the barber's hand stopped. The lather had turned a deep red. How horrible! What could he have done?

"Have you a small cut on your face anywhere, sir?" he stammered.

"Cut on my face? Certainly not, Turner. Unless you cut me yourself."

"But I haven't used the razor yet, sir. Here is a mirror," and he held a small hand glass in front of the great gentleman.

Catching sight of his face, Sir Geoffrey Wickersham roared like a bull. "Why, I look like a turkey cock — or a boy on Guy Fawkes night! What have you been doing to me, you rascal? Don't you know your trade any better than this? You have poisoned me!"

Puffing and panting with rage, he was about to rise from the chair when Turner said quietly, "Stay a moment, sir, if you please. I think I know what has happened. My boy has been using this brush. One moment only, sir — "

The barber carefully wiped off the red lather, made a fresh lot, and picked up another brush. By working rapidly he managed to smooth down the temper of his angry customer. Inwardly, he was very much disturbed. When Sir Geoffrey Wickersham was shaven clean, he

344

wished his hair dressed. After that was finished he said, "I'd give that boy a good beating, if he belonged to me. What was he doing?"

"Painting, sir. Really, his pictures are good. Let me tell you, sir, that once I took William, at five years old, to the house of a nobleman. The child had to sit on a chair in a corner while I dressed his lordship's hair. There was a silver tray with a coat of arms on it, a lion, standing against the wall of the room. William never took his eyes from that lion and when we came home he drew it perfectly. That convinced me that he ought to be a painter. See, I have some of his pictures in my shop here and I sometimes sell one for a few pence." He proudly pointed to sketches hanging among the wigs on his shop walls.

Sir Geoffrey looked down his nose at the paintings. "Better if you made a barber out of him, or a cobbler! Yet I suppose, as a barber, he'd brush his customers with all colors of the rainbow."

"Thank you, sir. No, sir. I'm afraid he wouldn't make a good barber. He'd best stick to his painting." Seeing his customer out with a bow, William Turner hurried back to his work, relieved that he had not lost both customer and fee.

Young William returned from school very much pleased about something and burst into the shop, eager to tell his father. His eyes were shining, and his feet barely touched the earth. But he found his father unusually serious and stern. For the moment, there were no customers in the shop.

"Come here, boy," said William Turner. "Did I give you leave to borrow my shaving brush yesterday? Think twice before you do such a thing again. I nearly lost one of my best customers."

William hung his head. "I'm sorry, Father, but you were out," he explained, "and I did return the brush as soon as I had finished the picture."

"Yes. Full of red paint!"

His son looked very much ashamed, and all the fresh color went out of his cheeks.

His father continued with better humor. "I was minded to punish you, William, but I'll think of a better way. How would it be if you did no painting for a fortnight?"

William looked ashamed, yet his eyes were still shining. "I've not told you the good news," he said.

"What good news?" Turner's voice was crisp.

"I carried last night's sunset piece to the school and the master was greatly taken with it. He says I should study under a London master and that he is going to ask one of his patrons to help me. He is coming to see you today."

The barber's look of worry began to fade, and the lines in his face softened. After all, he reflected, his son

346

must be a smart lad to win such praise from his school-master. Maybe there was more to this painting than he had thought. Suppose his William's work should fetch big prices one day! He could not foresee that next year, at twelve years old, his boy would study under a London teacher, and, at fourteen, enter the Royal Academy.

Just now he clapped his William on the back. "Up-stairs with you, you rascal, and change your coat for our visitor. Get your face and hands washed and the fire mended and the kettle put on to boil — and buy some cake. All's well that ends well. I've not lost a fee, and the brush is clean again. Only remember not to play such a trick on me a second time."

William nodded. His feet clattered merrily up the stairs.

Turner gazed toward the river that had been the source of all his boy's inspiration. He was thinking to himself that a boy who could bring color and warmth into a dull scene must be a pretty good painter after all. The sunset picture warmed the heart. He looked with puzzled wonder at the brush that had accomplished it, before he laid it, almost humbly, back on the table.

Laura Benét

THE UNBLAZED TRAIL

A Brave Boast

THE snowstorm, which had continued for a week, finally came to an end. The sun ventured over the horizon. In the forest the ptarmigan fluttered their white feathers. Signs of spring were in the air of Norway.

It was noon and the boys were out upon the Long Hill with their skis. They were talking about the coming vacation. All of those on the honor roll were invited to spend their holidays at the hunting lodge of Doctor Karl Hansen, whose son was one of the students at the school. Roald Amundsen, however, was not an honor student.

"Too bad you can't go with us," said young Karl, "but father never invites anyone who is not on the honor roll."

"Oh, you need not waste any pity on me," declared Roald. "I'm not going to be a doctor anyway."

"What are you going to be then?" cried one of the boys. The others gathered around to hear Roald's answer.

Roald fastened his ski-strap and rose to his feet. "I'm going to be an explorer," he said.

At this announcement the boys broke into laughter and jeers. "He is going to be an explorer. What an idea! You won't even cross Hellberget, you won't," they cried.

348

"Before you start boasting about what you are going to do, try your luck on that mountain," said young Karl. "In the history of Norway so far, no one has yet climbed it in the winter and gone down the other side to the sea."

Hellberget! After the boys had left him, Roald stood thinking about what they had said. No matter how foolish it seemed to them, he was going to be an explorer. If he could cross Hellberget, his companions could no longer make fun of his plans for the future.

At that moment his good friend Thorstein came up. "Why do you care what those fellows say?" he asked.

Roald stared at Thorstein as though he were seeing him for the first time.

"Shake!" he cried, putting out an eager hand. Then his words began tumbling over one another. "Did you

hear what they said about Hellberget? It has never yet been crossed by anyone at this time of the year. What do you think they would say if I crossed it during spring vacation?"

"Why can't we cross it together?" Thorstein asked. "The only thing we'll have to fight is the weather."

The agreement was made between the two, and on the day when the other boys left for the hunting lodge in the hills, Roald and Thorstein struck off for the west coast. Each of them carried a reindeer sleeping bag, an alcohol lamp, a pan, some goat cheese, and a little bread.

By consulting the map, they discovered that a farm called Garen lay on the west side of the mountain, and another called Magen on the east side. On top of the mountain there was a herd hut which the Lapps used in the summer.

The day was so clear that the mountains were sharply outlined against the sky. There was a fresh, crisp feel to the air. It was the kind of day when big new things should be started. They both agreed on that.

Roald and Thorstein easily reached Magen, the farm on the east side of the mountain. The people who lived there rarely saw strangers. They welcomed the boys and made haste to set the coffee pot on the stove and to prepare something warm for them to eat. But when they heard what the boys had in mind they all protested.

"If you try to make the other side of Hellberget at this time of year, the priest will be preaching your funeral services in the spring," said they. "If there were a way of getting over to Garen, some of our men, who are hardened to snow and wind, would have made it long before this."

"But they did not want to be explorers," Roald argued. "I do. I am going to find the Northwest Passage some day. Crossing Hellberget won't be much compared with that task. We can reach Garen in two days."

"And I'm going to fly a machine over the Doverfjeld when I grow up," Thorstein said. "Hellberget, after all, is not so much."

"At least you should take more food with you. What if you don't make Garen in two days?"

"We'll make it, never fear," the two boys repeated, and away they went.

It was bright and warm, and the breeze which pulled at their sleeves was playful and had the promise of spring in it. When noon came, the two boys sat down and ate their lunch. The afternoon was before them. They had followed the compass carefully and were sure they could make the herd hut by evening.

However, there was something about the air that made Roald anxious. It was too soft. When the air became so soft at this time of the year it was sometimes a bad sign.

The Norwegian afternoon was short. Suddenly the

351

moon shone above them and the shadows began playing pranks with them. They should have reached the herd hut by now. Roald was disappointed. Was it possible that he, who was going to be an explorer, had not been able to read the compass correctly?

He shaded his eyes against the star-glow and peered into the distance. What was that he saw? "It's the herd hut," he cried. "We've reached it at last."

Both of the boys were delighted.

When they came to the hut they set down their packs. Thorstein climbed up on the roof and removed the cap on the chimney, while Roald struggled to light a fire upon the open hearth. At last the chimney became warm enough to let the smoke rise.

When at length the blaze was roaring up the chimney, the two boys felt better. They saved a sandwich for lunch the next day, and, because they were so hungry, ate the rest.

"One sandwich will be enough tomorrow," they told each other confidently. "We'll be at Garen tomorrow night."

With that they banked the fire and got into their sleeping bags. During the night they woke up several times. A wind had come up and was roaring so fiercely about the corners of the roof that it seemed as if it might blow the hut away.

THE BLIZZARD

When Roald woke at seven he cried, "Thorstein! We'll have to get moving. It is seven o'clock."

Kicking out of their bags, they went to the door and struggled to open it. They had to thump and kick at it and when finally they got it open, they found that snow had begun to fall in the night. The wind had whipped up a blizzard. They could not see three feet before them. Well, they had not counted on this sort of thing. Halfway to Garen and this had to happen!

"I guess the only thing we can do is wait here until the storm passes," Roald said slowly.

"But what about food?" Thorstein asked. "We have only the chocolate we saved for breakfast and a sandwich apiece."

"We'll look about," Roald suggested. "The herders who were here last summer may have left something we can use for food."

In the loft they found a tin of rye flour. "We can make some water-porridge," Roald said. "There are plenty of people in Norway who have little else to eat in the winter."

So they made water-porridge, and, eating it, waited for the blizzard to die down. Instead it became worse. The

wind shook the hut so that it rocked and swayed. All day they sat by the fire, thankful for the supply of wood that the herders had laid in the summer before. The second day was just as wild as the first.

The morning of the third day, the wind died down but there was so much snow that they had to struggle to open the cabin door. The snow was so light that they would not be able to make any great speed, but they could not stay in the hut any longer. Taking their course by the compass, they set out. The gale seemed to be blowing from every direction. When at length the wind fell, the snow began again. They took their map and tried to follow it,

but the flakes were wet, and the map was soon soaked and useless.

"We might as well throw this thing away," Roald had to say at last. "I can't make out a single line of it."

Suddenly, as though luck had deserted them, the needle of the compass began rocking and spinning about crazily.

"It must be the ore deposits in the mountain," Roald said with a groan. "We can't trust it any longer."

They had nothing now to guide them except their own sense of direction, and in such a storm as this they could not count too much on that. Night came again, this time without even a herder's hut for shelter.

"We should be near Garen," Roald declared, but the wind carried his words off across the drifts so that his companion could only guess at their meaning.

They pushed on, side by side, until suddenly Roald found himself alone. Realizing that his friend had gone over a cliff, he flung himself down upon his skis to stop himself before he, too, should go over. He was not a moment too soon, for at that instant he heard a voice from below, "I've gone over a cliff. Don't go any farther."

As luck would have it, Thorstein had fallen upon his back and his pack had broken the fall. When he had climbed back to the ledge above, both boys realized it would not be safe to go any farther in the dark, and so they decided to dig in where they were for the night.

They had not eaten their sandwiches. Now, in the face of their danger, they had no desire to eat. They took the food from their pockets, and set it down in one place together with their alcohol lamps and the compass. Then they stood up a ski-pole beside these things to mark the spot. Pulling their sleeping bags over them, they prepared for the night.

Their garments had been wet, and before long the boys were damp to the skin. But somehow they slept until, during the night, Roald was awakened by the chill. His fingers ached with the cold. His feet were numb. Suddenly he thought of the alcohol lamp. He would get up and light

356

it. That would surely give a little heat. But he could find neither the ski-pole which had been set up as marker nor anything else.

He awakened Thorstein. They both made a search of the snow. Their food, the compass, and the alcohol lamps had completely vanished. Cold as the boys were, they did not dare crawl back into their bags. Instead, they stamped about in a circle until it became daylight.

"Garen must be here somewhere," Roald said. "I feel it in my bones."

When morning came, they pushed on and on, through the endless white drifts of the snow. They were hungry, too. How they regretted not eating their sandwiches!

They came to springs of water dripping down the side of the mountain. They drank of the water and were thankful for it. Finally Roald stopped.

"We are lost," he said. "We should have reached Garen long ago. Since we have not, there is only one thing to do. We must try to retrace our steps."

"Go back!" Thorstein's words sounded hollow.

Roald smiled a crooked smile. "I guess I'm not so good as I thought," he said.

They turned back. All that day they pushed on. Their legs felt as though they had grown longer, much longer and very, very thin. The hollow feeling in their stomachs had grown so enormous that it seemed to include the whole

357

of them. However, they said nothing to each other of how they felt.

Night came again. They found the lee side of a drift and Roald dug out a hollow in the bank big enough for him to crawl into. Then he stuck his feet into his sleeping bag and pulled it in over him. The snow deadened the sound of the wind outside. The place seemed warm. Roald would have been comfortable had he not been so hungry.

Roald woke up once. The snow was soft under him and he went to sleep again. The next time he woke up he felt cramped. He tried to turn and discovered that his sleeping bag was frozen to the ice beneath him. The warmth from his breath had melted the snow about him and this, in turn, had frozen as the night became colder. He shouted for his companion but there was no answer. The snow had heaped up about the entrance to his cave. Overtaken by a feeling of suffocation, he tried to struggle out of the bag. It was no use. A slow darkness closed over him.

In the meantime, Thorstein woke up. The stars were bright overhead. It was almost as light as day. He looked about for his companion. Roald was nowhere to be seen. Desperately Thorstein began clawing at the snow. Surely the wind had not blown Roald away! Thorstein struck about with his ski-pole and suddenly saw a few reindeer hairs sticking out of the snow. He scraped away the snow, and discovered the end of Roald's sleeping bag.

When Roald had been dragged out of his cave and revived, both boys were too frightened to lie down again. They got upon their skies and, guiding their course by the stars, pushed on to the eastward.

It was seven days from the time they had started when they suddenly came upon a hay shed. There were ski-tracks around it. They had reached civilization again!

To their surprise the boys found that they had returned to a place only a half mile from the farm they had left eight days before. Before long they again stood before the hearth and warmed their hands at the fire. But they had become so snow-blackened and so thin that no one knew they were the same two boys who had started off to the westward a week before.

Sadly, the boys took the boat home. Roald was bitterly disappointed. He had set out to reach Garen. His very first expedition had failed. On the way home, the steamer put in at Kampfiord to pick up a few passengers.

One of these, a fisherman, started a conversation with the boys. "I never believed in troll-folk before," said he, "but something happened at Garen a few days ago which makes me wonder."

"Garen!" cried the boys. "What happened?"

"I came upon ski-tracks from the east behind my stable. They struck off toward the sea for a hundred yards or more and then they turned and led off to the east again." He shook his head. "No one has ever seen ski-tracks from the east in the winter before," he added, a puzzled look in his eyes.

The two boys stared at each other in amazement. "Our ski-tracks!" they said. "We did reach Garen." They had not failed in what they set out to do, after all.

Nora Burglon

360

SIGHTS AND SOUNDS

THE WIND AND THE MOON

Said the Wind to the Moon, "I will blow you out;
>　You stare
>　In the air
>　Like a ghost in a chair,
Always looking what I am about —
I hate to be watched; I'll blow you out."

The Wind blew hard, and out went the Moon.
>　So deep
>　On a heap
>　Of clouds to sleep,
Down lay the Wind, and slumbered soon,
Muttering low, "I've done for that Moon."

He turned in his bed; she was there again!
>　On high
>　In the sky,
>　With her one ghost eye,
The Moon shone white and alive and plain.
Said the Wind, "I will blow you out again."

362

The Wind blew hard, and the Moon grew dim.
      "With my sledge,
      And my wedge,
      I have knocked off her edge!
If only I blow right fierce and grim,
The creature will soon be dimmer than dim."

He blew and he blew, and she thinned to a thread.
      "One puff
      More's enough
      To blow her to snuff!
One good puff more where the last was bred,
And glimmer, glimmer, glum will go the thread."

He blew a great blast, and the thread was gone.
      In the air
      Nowhere
      Was a moonbeam bare;
Far off and harmless the shy stars shone —
Sure and certain the Moon was gone!

The Wind he took to his revels once more;
      On down,
      In town,
      Like a merry-mad clown,
He leaped and hallooed with whistle and roar —
"What's that?" The glimmering thread once more!

He flew in a rage — he danced and blew;
        But in vain
        Was the pain
        Of his bursting brain;
For still the broader the Moon-scrap grew,
The broader he swelled his big cheeks and blew.

Slowly she grew — till she filled the night,
        And shone
        On her throne
        In the sky alone,
A matchless, wonderful, silvery light,
Radiant and lovely, the queen of the night.

Said the Wind: "What a marvel of power am I!
        With my breath,
        Good faith!
        I blew her to death —
First blew her away right out of the sky —
Then blew her in; what strength have I!"

But the Moon she knew nothing about the affair;
        For high
        In the sky,
        With her one white eye,
Motionless, miles above the air,
She had never heard the great Wind blare.

George Macdonald

TO A BUTTERFLY

I've watched you now a full half hour,
Self-poised upon that yellow flower;
And, little butterfly, indeed,
I know not if you sleep or feed.

How motionless! — not frozen seas
    More motionless; and then,
What joy awaits you when the breeze
Hath found you out among the trees,
    And calls you forth again!

This plot of orchard ground is ours,
My trees they are, my sister's flowers;
Here rest your wings when they are weary,
Here lodge as in a sanctuary!

Come to us often, fear no wrong,
    Sit near us on the bough!
We'll talk of sunshine and of song,
And summer days when we were young;
Sweet childish days that were as long
    As twenty days are now.

William Wordsworth

THE WAGON IN THE BARN

THERE are mushrooms in the paddock,
  And walnuts on the trees,
And a hive in the corner
  To keep the honey-bees;
There's a hay-rick in the rick-yard,
  And another one of wheat,
And there are cooking apples,
  And other ones to eat.

There are berries on the bushes,
  The yellow ones and red,
There are starlings in the willows,
  And swallows in the shed;
There's a scarecrow in the garden,
  With a patch upon his "starn."
But the thing that I like best is
  The wagon in the barn.

For in the rainy weather,
   We all climb up inside,
And we have a team of horses
   To take us for a ride;
And although they think we're playing
   In the barn because it rains,
We go riding in the wagon
   For miles along the lanes.

John Drinkwater

THE SHELL

AND then I pressed the shell
Close to my ear
And listened well,
And straightway, like a bell,
Came low and clear
The slow, sad murmur of far-distant seas,
Whipped by an icy breeze
Upon a shore
Windswept and desolate.
It was a sunless strand that never bore
The footprint of a man,
Nor felt the weight,
Since time began,
Of any human quality or stir
Save what the dreary winds and waves incur.
And in the hush of waters was the sound
Of pebbles rolling round,
Forever rolling with a hollow sound.

And bubbling seaweeds, as the waters go,
Swished to and fro
Their long tentacles of slimy gray.
There was no day,
Nor ever came a night,
Setting the stars alight,
To wonder at the moon.
Was twilight only and the frightened croon,
Smitten to whimpers, of the dreary wind
And waves that journeyed blind . . .
And then I loosed my ear — oh, it was sweet
To hear a cart go jolting down the street.

James Stephens

FIRE

"FIRE, you have been a servant,
Kind and good,
Warming all within this household,
Baking food.
For two hundred years, and more too,
You have sung
Like a nurse beside the cradle
Of the young."

But the fire never hearkened,
Never stayed.
Up the shrinking walls its terrible
Path was made.
On the roof it leaped and capered,
Faster, faster,
Like a mad thing, laughing, panting —
"Now, I'm master!"

Elizabeth Coatsworth

FESTIVAL TIME

THE MAKING OF A SAILOR

WHAT sort of lad was Columbus? This problem worried me when I was a boy. My schoolbook said that
no one knew the exact date of Columbus's birth. Also it
told nothing about his boyhood. The first really important
thing seemed to be that he told the queen he thought he
could find China by sailing to the west. Then she sold
her jewels and gave him the money to buy three ships,
with which he discovered America. Then, for the first
time, said my schoolbook, men in general believed the
world was round.

It seemed a queer business, so I wondered what sort of
lad Columbus was, and that wondering fitted itself into a
kind of sing-song:

> What sort of lad was Columbus?
> What sort of lad was Columbus?
> What sort of lad, what sort of lad,
> What sort of lad was Columbus?

For one thing, he seemed to be able, I thought, to persuade people, for if men really believed that the world was
flat and that there was a place where the sea ran over a cliff,

then the sailors must have been very brave or very foolish to sail west. That worried me.

It worried me until, years later, I found that young Columbus had a relative named Uncle Colombo who was a sailor and had sailed with Arabs, and who was very fond of young Christopher Columbus. Now both the Greeks and the Arabs, many hundreds of years before Columbus was born, had not only taught that the world was round, but that it measured twenty-four thousand miles, which was nearly right. So, since Arabs and Greeks, who were great seamen, knew it, and since they sailed with Moors, Italians, Spaniards, and others, then what they knew, their shipmates must have known. For that reason it was not likely that any Mediterranean sailor would be afraid of sailing over the edge of the world. Certainly Uncle Colombo would have laughed at the idea, and so would his favorite, young Christopher.

It is true that no one knows the date of Columbus's birth, but it was somewhere between 1435 and 1451. We must see him as a boy tall for his age, fair-skinned and bright-eyed, much given to wandering down to the port to look at ships and listen to sailors' talk. That interested him more than the weaving in his father's shop. As he was fond of hearing about travel and adventure, it came natural to him to like geography; and liking geography, he naturally liked maps.

So, when the chance came for him to help a map maker, he seized it eagerly. There were good maps in those days. We can picture young Columbus looking at the maps and taking imaginary voyages, as many a boy has done. Work on maps, it need hardly be said, helped to make him interested in geometry and astronomy. It came about naturally that he learned Latin, enjoyed reading, and took an interest in science, especially navigation. He was one of those happy lads who are interested in many things, and for whom every day is a new adventure.

One happy day, we are told, Uncle Colombo asked the fourteen-year-old boy if he would like to take a sea trip. We know what answer would be given. Young Christopher, however, could not go as a passenger. He had to take his place with other ship's boys of his own age, or older, doing what had to be done with hearty good will and taking the rough with the smooth. But there is this to be remembered: while other boys may have had more experience, young Christopher knew more than they, and that counted for much. He could find a ship's position with instruments. He could read a chart and he could make one. He could do a little more than he was expected to do, which always counts, on shore as well as on sea.

We have to think of him as we think of young Farragut, who was in command of men aboard ship at the age of eleven. We have to think of him as we think of young

Mozart, who played the piano like a master at the age of seven, or of Alexander, who led armies before he was twenty, or William Cullen Bryant, who was a poet at fourteen.

The young Columbus made many voyages with Uncle Colombo and some without. In those days, to be a sailor in the Mediterranean was almost like being a soldier too. Pirates lurked everywhere, and nations were at war, so that every ship went armed, and every man and boy had to be ready to fight. There came a time when young Columbus was in charge of a ship and was sent to capture the galley *Fernandino*, then in the Bay of Tunis. The *Fernandino* was a pirate craft that had done mischief and was likely to do more. The story of that voyage is an exciting one and too long to tell here. You may be sure that Columbus showed himself both brave and wise on this adventure, which would have proved difficult even for a much older and more experienced commander.

A later voyage ended less happily. The vessel burned after a terrible sea fight, and Columbus was forced to leap into the sea. He was lucky enough to find a drifting oar and with its help got safely to land and to the city of Lisbon.

Though he had arrived there through accident, the young man wasted no time, but turned his hand to one of his many trades, this time that of map maker. There, too, he presently married, and, though his earnings were small, he was able to send a little money to his father to help his younger brothers through school.

Columbus made still other journeys before the historical one across the Atlantic in 1492. He sailed back and forth between Guinea, in Africa, and Portugal. He made a voyage or two to England and to Iceland. We have his own word for that last.

"I navigated," Columbus wrote, "in the month of February, 1477, as far as a hundred leagues beyond the island of Tile, whose southern part is at latitude 73°. The island is large as England. The English, especially those of Bristol, go there to trade. When I was there the sea was not frozen over."

We know, too, from early records, that Columbus was

in Bristol in the year 1486, where John Cabot, of Genoa, was a merchant. This was the same Cabot who discovered Newfoundland and Nova Scotia in 1498. It is likely that Columbus and Cabot met and talked about voyages, but that is only a guess. Still, birds of a feather do flock together, and Bristol was no very large town.

And now comes a wonderful thing, if a certain Frenchman named M. Roncière is right.

That Frenchman was, not long ago, the historian of the French navy, so his words are worth weighing. We know that in 1491, when Columbus went to Ferdinand and Isabella, the king and queen, to tell them of his wish to go west, he showed them a map. We know nothing about the map, but we remember that Columbus was a map maker.

Back in 1849, a strange old colored map turned up in Paris and was bought by the National Library. No one took much notice of it until M. Roncière made a careful study of it. He came to believe that it was the map that Columbus made himself and took to the king and queen. It does not, of course, show any land where America would be, but it does show Greenland. And this is written on it where Iceland is shown: "An island full of mountains and snow and ice, with an ever severe climate, called Iceland in the local language, and Tile in Latin. There, at a great distance from the British Island, on account of the cold, no other food is to be had but fish frozen. The natives exchange them for wheat and flour . . . that the English bring them every year. It is a rugged and wild population . . ."

What sort of lad was Columbus? Taking one thing with another, we must see him as one who became master of himself. He saw straight. He noted what he saw. He thought. He planned. He listened to others who knew. He had faith in himself. He gathered facts, saw to what they led, then acted.

When people, whether old or young, make of themselves the best that they may become, they very often do more than they expect to do, and more than we expect they could do. Columbus thought he would sail to China, and would have done so, only he found a continent, which was certainly more than he expected.

Charles J. Finger

CHRISTOPHER COLUMBUS

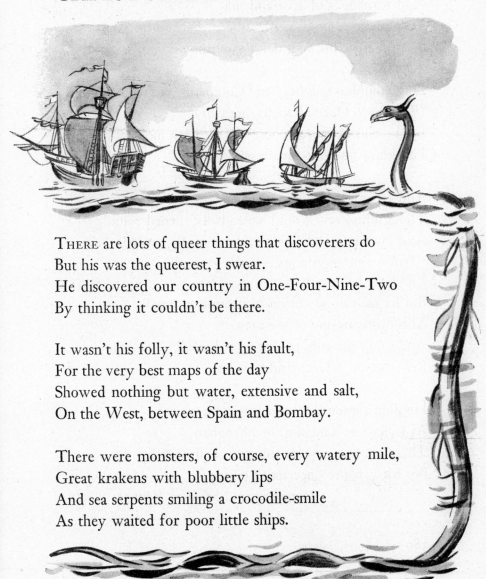

THERE are lots of queer things that discoverers do
But his was the queerest, I swear.
He discovered our country in One-Four-Nine-Two
By thinking it couldn't be there.

It wasn't his folly, it wasn't his fault,
For the very best maps of the day
Showed nothing but water, extensive and salt,
On the West, between Spain and Bombay.

There were monsters, of course, every watery mile,
Great krakens with blubbery lips
And sea serpents smiling a crocodile-smile
As they waited for poor little ships.

There were whirlpools and maelstroms, without any doubt,
And tornadoes of lava and ink.
(Which, as nobody yet had been there to find out,
Seems a little bit odd, don't you think?)

But Columbus was bold and Columbus set sail
(Thanks to Queen Isabella, her pelf),
For he said, "Though there may be both monster and gale,
I'd like to find out for myself."

And he sailed and he sailed and he sailed and he sailed,
Though his crew would have gladly turned round
And, morning and evening, distressfully wailed,
"This is running things into the ground!"

But he paid no attention to protest or squall,
This obstinate son of the mast,
And so, in the end, he discovered us all,
Remarking, "Here's India, at last!"

He didn't intend it, he meant to heave to
At Calcutta, Rangoon, or Shanghai.
There are many queer things that discoverers do,
But his was the queerest. Oh, my!

                    Rosemary and *Stephen Vincent Benét*

THE LOG OF COLUMBUS

This is the log of Christopher Columbus as copied out in brief by his companion, Bartholomew Las Casas.

Wednesday, October 10, 1492.

Steered W. S. W. and sailed at times ten miles an hour, at others twelve, and at others seven. Day and night, made fifty-nine leagues' progress. Reckoned to the crew but forty-four. Here the men could bear no more and complained of the length of the voyage. But the Admiral encouraged them in the best way he could, giving them good hope of the advantages they might gain. He added that however much they might complain, having come so far, he had nothing to do but go to the Indies, and he would go on until he found them, with the help of Our Lord.

Thursday, October 11, 1492.

Steered W. S. W. There was a heavier sea than had been met with before in the whole voyage. Saw sandpipers and a green rush near the vessel. The crew of the *Pinta* saw a cane and a log. They also picked up a stick which appeared to have been carved with an iron, a piece of cane, a plant which grows on land, and a board. The crew of the *Niña* saw other signs of land and a stalk loaded with roseberries. Everyone breathed afresh and rejoiced at these signs. Sailed this day till sunset, twenty-seven leagues.

After sunset steered their original course W. and sailed twelve miles an hour till two hours after midnight, going twenty-two leagues and a half. As the *Pinta* was the swiftest sailer and kept ahead of the Admiral, she discovered land and made the signals ordered by the Admiral. The land was first seen by a sailor called Rodrigo de Triana, although the Admiral at ten o'clock that evening, being on the castle of the poop, saw a light, but so small a body that he could not affirm it to be land. Calling to Pero Gutierrez, gentleman of the King's bedchamber, he told him he saw light and bid him look that way, which he did and saw it.

After the Admiral had spoken he saw the light once or twice again, appearing and disappearing like the light of a wax candle moving up and down. Few thought this an indication of land, but the Admiral held it for certain that land was near. For which reason, after they had said the *Salve* which the seamen are accustomed to repeat and chant after their fashion, the Admiral directed them to keep a strict watch upon the forecastle and to watch well for land. To him who should first cry out that he saw land he said he would give a silken doublet besides the reward of ten thousand maravedis a year which the King and Queen had offered.

At two o'clock in the morning the land was sighted at the distance of two leagues. Shortened sail, remaining under the square-sail. The vessels were hove to, waiting for daylight.

Friday, October 12, 1492.

When it grew light they found themselves near a small island, one of the Lucayos, called in the Indian language Guanahani. Presently they saw people, naked, and the Admiral went on shore in the armed boat, along with Martin Alonzo Pinzon, and Vincent Yanez, his brother, Captain of the *Niña*. The Admiral bore the royal standard, and the two captains each carried a banner of the Green Cross, which all the ships had carried. This contained the initials of the names of the King and Queen each side of the cross, and a crown over each letter.

Arrived on shore, they saw trees very green, many streams of water, and fruits of many kinds. The Admiral called to the two captains, and to others who leaped on shore, and to Rodrigo de Escovedo, secretary of the whole fleet, and to Rodrigo Sanchez, of Segovia, to bear witness that before all others he took possession (as in fact he now did) of that island for the King and Queen, his sovereigns, making the declarations that are required, as is mostly set down in testimonies which were then made in writing. Presently large numbers of the inhabitants crowded to the shores.

Here follow the actual words of the Admiral:

"As I saw that they were very friendly to us and perceived that they could be much more easily converted to our holy faith by gentle means than by force, I presented them with some red caps, and strings of glass beads to put round their necks, and many other trifles of small value, which gave them great pleasure. Wherewith they were much delighted, and this made them so much our friends that it was a marvel to see. Afterwards they came swimming to the boats, bringing parrots, balls of cotton thread, javelins, and many other things which they exchanged for articles we gave them, such as glass beads and hawks' bells. In fine, they took all and gave what they had with good will. But they seemed on the whole to me to be a very poor people.

"They all go as naked as when their mothers bore them, even the women, though I saw but one girl. All whom I saw were young, not above thirty years of age, well made, with fine shapes and faces. Their hair is short, and coarse like that of a horse's tail. They wear the hairs brought down to the eyebrows combed towards the forehead, except a few locks behind, which they wear long and never cut. Some paint themselves black, some paint themselves white, others red, and others such colors as they can find. They are like the Canarians, neither black nor white.

384

"Weapons they have none, nor are acquainted with them, for I showed them swords, which they grasped by the blades and cut themselves through ignorance. They have no iron, their darts being wands without iron and nothing more than sticks. Some of them have a fish's tooth at the end, others being pointed in various ways. The people are all of a good size and stature, with good faces and well made.

"I saw some with scars of wounds upon their bodies, and asked by signs the cause of them. They answered me in the same way that there came people from other islands in the neighborhood with the intention of seizing them, and they defended themselves. I thought then, and still believe, that these came from the mainland to take them prisoners.

"It appears to me that the people are ingenious and would be good servants, and I am of opinion that they would very readily become Christians, as they appear to have no religion. They very quickly learn such words as are spoken to them. If it please Our Lord, I intend at my return to carry home six of them to Your Highnesses, that they may learn our language. I saw no beasts on this island of any kind, except parrots."

These are the words of the Admiral.

JACK O'LANTERN

A PUMPKIN, a mumpkin,
A jilly jolly jumpkin,
We'll make a jack o'lantern,
For this is Hallowe'en.
We'll hang it round the corner,
To fright the Brownie Bumpkin,
And scare the little goblins,
That gobble on the green.

A pumpkin, a mumpkin,
A jilly jolly jumpkin,
Eyes, nose, and mouth now,
With teeth grinning wide.
Scoop him out clean,
With a scrape and a scrumpkin,
And put a lighted candle
In his little inside.

Laura E. Richards

PHANTOM CATS

Long, long ago, as you have often heard, there were fairies and giants and ogres and dragons. There were gallant young knights looking for brave deeds to do. There were lovely maidens waiting to be rescued from fearful dangers.

In those good old days in the long, long ago, the young warrior of whom I am about to tell you started forth in search of dangerous deeds in which he might prove himself wise and brave and strong.

The young warrior went on for some time meeting nothing out of the ordinary. He crossed bubbling streams and rushing rivers. He climbed mountains and waded through grass-grown meadows. But he met no thrilling adventure.

One morning he found himself in a deep forest.

"Surely I shall find something to prove my bravery in this gloomy forest," said the young warrior to himself.

But all day long he traveled through the thick woods without meeting anything to test his bravery. He found himself at evening on a lonely mountain on the edge of the forest.

The young warrior looked in every direction. It was

indeed a lonely spot. No sign of human beings was to be seen. No village, no cottage was in sight. There was not even a charcoal burner's hut, such as may almost always be found by the outer rim of the forest.

For a time the young warrior followed a very faint footpath. Finally he lost sight even of that. Each effort seemed to entangle him more hopelessly in the briars and thorny shrubs and tall grasses. Faint and weary, the young warrior stumbled on through the growing darkness.

Suddenly, when he was about to drop with weariness, he came upon a little temple. It was a strange place for a temple, but the young warrior was so tired that he scarcely thought of that. The building was deserted and half ruined. The walls in places were quite broken. But at the farther end still stood a shrine.

"Here at least is shelter," said the young man to himself. "Here I shall pass the night. To be sure, I have no food, but I'm thankful for a sheltered place in which to sleep."

So saying, he wrapped his long mantle about him more closely. He placed his good sword by his side, where it might be ready in case of need. Then, with his arm under his head for a pillow, he was soon fast asleep.

It was nearly midnight when the young warrior wakened with a start. What was that dreadful noise? Had he been dreaming? And was he still asleep?

389

At first he thought it could be nothing but a hideous dream. The noise not only continued, but it grew worse. Soon the whole place was echoing with shrieks and yells. Then he knew it was no dream.

Cautiously he raised himself. He seized his good sword in his strong right hand. Then he dragged himself, without making the least noise, to a hole in the ruined wall. He peered through the hole into a deserted court. He beheld a strange and dreadful sight!

There was a great company of hideous cats. They were dancing wildly. They were screaming and yelling and making the night horrible with their cries.

Presently he seemed to catch words amid the babel. He listened more closely. He strained every nerve to make out the words. At last they came quite clearly:

"Tell it not to Schippietaro,
Keep it close and dark!
Tell it not to Schippietaro,
Keep it close and dark!"

What could it all mean? Who was Schippietaro? What was the secret which Schippietaro was not to know?

Still the hideous shrieking and yelling continued. Still through that noise came the words of the strange song.

It was a horrible scene. Every cat looked as black as the darkness of the thick forest in the clear light of the full moon. The sound was awful.

Suddenly, as the midnight hour passed, silence fell on the temple. The strange cat army disappeared as if by magic. All was still and the full moon shone down on the quiet court.

The young warrior again drew his mantle about him and prepared to rest. The remainder of the night passed quietly, and he slept undisturbed until morning.

With the sun the young warrior arose. In the bright light of morning he soon discovered the path which he had lost the night before.

He feared that it led again into the forest through which he had already passed. But in a little while, to his great joy, he came out on an open plain. Close by was a cottage or two. Farther on was a village.

"In the village I shall find food," said the warrior to himself, and being very hungry, he pressed on eagerly.

As he was swinging on with great strides toward the village, he was stopped by the sound of a woman's voice crying bitterly.

At the cry of grief the young warrior forgot his hunger and turned aside to find what the matter might be, and if possible, to give help.

He hastened to the nearest cottage. He asked many questions of the sad people there.

"The time has come," they said, "when the Mountain Spirit claims its victim. Once every year this happens. Tonight, when the moon rises, he will take our loveliest maiden to his mountain home. There he will destroy her. This is the reason for our grief. There is no help for it. The maiden must die."

The young warrior was more than ever filled with wonder. He asked for further information.

At sunset, he was told, the victim would be placed in a sort of golden cage. Then she would be carried to the very ruined temple in which he himself had passed the night. There she would be left alone.

In the morning, they said, the maiden would have vanished. The Mountain Spirit would have claimed her. As it had happened each year, so it would happen tonight. There was no help for it. Then they broke into fresh weeping.

"If I might but deliver the lovely maiden," thought the young warrior, "here indeed would be an adventure."

Again he thought of the ruined temple and of the shrine. Again he thought of the awful dance of the cats and their hideous cries. The words of their strange chant came back to him:

"Tell it not to Schippietaro,
    Keep it close and dark!
Tell it not to Schippietaro,
    Keep it close and dark!"

"Have you ever heard the name of Schippietaro?" he asked.

"Oh, yes," was the answer.

"Who and what is he?" asked the young man, more eagerly.

"Schippietaro is a great, beautiful dog," said they. "He belongs to our prince, who lives in a grand castle but a

short distance from here. We see Schippietaro often. He follows the prince everywhere. He is a brave, fine fellow, and he is afraid of nothing."

The young warrior asked no more questions. He asked for a guide to the prince's castle. He almost outran his guide, so eager was he to arrive at the castle.

He found the prince in the garden. A great beautiful dog lay at his feet. The young warrior went straight to the prince and asked if he might borrow Schippietaro for just one night.

At first the prince refused. He was unwilling to part with the dog for even one night. But the young warrior insisted. It was a case of life and death, he said, and he must have Schippietaro.

At last the prince consented on the condition that Schippietaro should be brought back unharmed the next day. Overjoyed, the young warrior led Schippietaro away.

With Schippietaro following, the young warrior next went to the home of the unhappy maiden chosen for this night's victim to the evil Mountain Spirit. He told the parents to keep their daughter in the house and to watch her carefully until his return.

Then he placed the dog Schippietaro in the golden cage intended for the maiden. With the help of some of the young men of the village, the cage was carried to the

394

temple. He bade the young men stay, but they refused. They ran in terror down the mountain as though a whole army of goblins were after them.

So the brave young warrior and the brave dog Schippietaro were left alone to see what would happen when the Mountain Spirit came to claim his victim.

They had not long to wait, for it was nearly midnight. The moon shone clear, as on the night before.

On the stroke of twelve came the company of cats. The young warrior could not see from what place they came, for all at once they appeared in the court.

At their head marched a huge black cat, ten times bigger and fiercer and blacker and more terrible than any of the others. The young warrior knew that this must be the Mountain Fiend himself.

When the leader caught sight of the cage he danced and yelled. The whole company took up the dance and the yelling. It was frightful. But the young warrior remained where he was hidden. Schippietaro made no sound.

When the great cat had danced and jeered at his victim until he was tired, he threw open the door of the cage and bade the lovely maiden to come forth.

But it was no lovely maiden who sprang into **the** arms of the great black cat. It was the brave Schippietaro. For once the Mountain Spirit had met his match.

Schippietaro sprang straight at the huge cat's throat and held him fast until the young warrior ran up. With one stroke of his sword he laid the monster dead.

As for the other cats, they were too astonished to move. They stood gazing at the body of their master. The warrior and the dog made short work of them.

At sunrise the young warrior returned the dog to the prince with a thousand thanks. He went to the parents of the maiden and told them that their daughter was quite safe. He told the people of the village that the Mountain Fiend had claimed his last victim and that he lay dead in the ruined temple.

Then the prince and the parents and all the village people tried to thank the brave young warrior.

"Nay," said he, laying his hand on the dog's furry neck, "you owe it all to your friend Schippietaro."

When the young warrior turned to leave the village, Schippietaro remained close to his side.

"Take him with you," said the prince, generously.

"No," said the young warrior. "Much would I like the brave dog, but you may need him to fight other battles for you."

So saying, the young warrior strode off alone through the sunshiny meadows in search of fresh adventures.

L. E. Mulets

FIVE EYES

In Hans' old mill, his three black cats
Watch the bins for the thieving rats.
Whisker and claw, they crouch in the night,
Their five eyes smoldering green and bright.
Squeaks from the flour sacks, squeaks from where
The cold wind stirs on the empty stair,
Squeaking and scampering, everywhere.
Then down they pounce, now in, now out,
At whisking tail and sniffling snout;
While lean old Hans, he snores away
Till peep of light at break of day;
Then up he climbs to his creaking mill,
Out come his cats all gray with meal —
Jekkel, and Jessup, and one-eyed Jill.

Walter de la Mare

THE VINLAND RIDDLE

Nobody knew what had become of the little black
hen. One minute she was in the fenced-in yard of
the Greenland farm home. The next minute she wasn't to
be seen. Astrid called and called and hunted and hunted,
but never a sign did she find of the little black hen.

The worst of it was that Astrid's father and mother
and Astrid herself were all ready to set sail for Vinland-
the-Good, a new land to the southwest of Greenland. It
had been discovered by Leif the Lucky.

Now many Vikings were going in their dragon boats to
the new land. They were taking cattle and sheep with
them in the boats, and Astrid had been promised that
she should take her special pet, the little black hen.
Astrid's cousin Siegfred was taking his old gray goose.

"You may share my goose," promised Siegfred, when
Astrid came weeping to the dragon boat. But sharing a

goose was not the same thing as taking one's own little black hen on the journey to the new land.

Old Olaf understood that. Olaf was sorry about the little black hen. "Probably she wanted to stay in Greenland," he said. And he brought Astrid a baby lamb to care for on the journey to Vinland-the-Good.

Then the Vikings raised the single sail at the mast of each dragon boat. The boats were called dragon boats because they had the head of a dragon carved at the bow while the tail of a dragon lifted above the water at the stern. The sails were made from the wool of the Greenland sheep and had been woven in bright-colored stripes by the women. Each boat had oars as well, many pairs of them. Now the wind filled the sails, the oars flashed in the sun, and the Vikings were on their way.

As they journeyed, Olaf, who was too old to row, began telling stories. The children loved old Olaf and his splendid tales. But most of all, Astrid and Siegfred loved the riddles he would ask them. Most of these riddles were so old that nobody knew when they were first told.

"What are the creatures that pass over lands, playing at will? They wear white shields in winter and dark ones in summer."

Siegfred guessed the answer, for he had seen ptarmigan, and knew that these birds have black feathers in summer and white ones in winter.

"What," asked Olaf, looking over the sea, "has a hard bed and is always restless?"

The answer was, "The waves of the sea."

But the riddle both children liked best of all was this:

"I went from home, I stood on a bridge,
I looked on the road of roads;
Road was above, road was beneath,
And road was in every direction."

This was the answer to the riddle:

"When you went from home
And stood on a bridge,
You looked on a river.
A bird flew above you;
His road was the air.
A fish swam beneath you;
His road was the river.
And the river — which for all Vikings
Is the road of roads —
The river flowed east and west.
But you stood on a bridge,
And the road over the bridge
Ran north and south;
So there were roads in all directions,
Over you, under you, on either hand."

400

When dusk fell and the Vikings lifted their oars and waited for the Steering Star to shine out in the north, Olaf would cuddle one of the children in either arm. Then he would tell them stories of the Vikings of northern Europe, who had sailed many seas in their dragon boats.

"The Vikings are fearless," declared Olaf, "and they are always ready to learn. They learned to steer by the stars and the sun. They found the lands of Ireland, Scotland, Normandy, and the lands, too, of Iceland and Greenland. They left their old homes in Europe and made themselves new homes in the lands they found.

"And last of all, Leif the Lucky, whose father discovered Greenland, found the western land which he named Vinland-the-Good, because the vines were plentiful there and it was a good land. Grain and wild grapes grew there, and tall trees. There was, he reported, plenty of grass for cattle to eat. "Indeed," ended Olaf, "I think this land to which we are going is the best land of all."

Astrid's eyes filled with tears. "I wish," she said, "my little black hen had come too."

"Tut, tut," said Olaf. "When Vikings left their old homes in Europe, they probably wished they could take with them all the things they loved. But they never could — not all. Now I shall tell you a riddle, Astrid. I myself do not know the answer. But sometime you will find the answer and tell it to me."

401

Astrid and Siegfred were looking at Olaf in amazement. How could he ask a riddle to which he himself did not know the answer?

"This is the riddle," said Olaf. "When is a pet hen not a hen?" His eyes twinkled so that Astrid laughed in spite of herself.

"How will you ever find the answer to that, Astrid?" asked Siegfred.

"I don't know," said Astrid. "Do you suppose there really is an answer?"

"My father says," declared Siegfred, "that Olaf is a very wise man."

At last the dragon boats came to Vinland, a part of the coast that centuries after was to be known as North America. The cows were taken off the boat. The little lambs were unloaded, and the big geese. Every time Astrid saw the geese she wondered about the riddle and longed for her little black hen.

But there was much to do in Vinland. While the men cut down the trees and built the log houses, the women and children gathered the ripe grain and berries that they found in the woods. The women dried fish, too, and made salt from the water of the sea. During the long winter that soon followed, the women carded and spun the wool they had brought with them.

As soon as spring came, the women and children went

forth looking for fresh green herbs that were good to eat, and they found many. Best of all, they thought, was the kind which bore a yellow blossom in its center. That blossom looked for all the world like a piece of golden money.

All this time Astrid tried to find the answer to Olaf's riddle. Olaf always told her, "Some day you will find it, Astrid. Of that I am very sure."

One day, when she and Siegfred were gathering wild berries along a Vinland brook, they came upon a nest, hidden in some long grasses. In the nest were thirteen eggs.

As Astrid bent over the nest, suddenly her eyes sparkled. "Siegfred," she said to her cousin, "I have an idea. This may be the answer to Olaf's riddle."

She whispered in Siegfred's ear. His eyes sparkled, too, as he listened. When Astrid and Siegfred went home, each of them carried an egg from the nest they had found.

Now Siegfred's old gray goose was setting on some eggs of her own. She made no protest whatsoever when the children slipped the eggs from the woods in under her. She simply spread her gray wings a little wider.

After what seemed to the children a long time, the gray goose hatched her own eggs, and she hatched also the two eggs that had been brought her from the woodland. The fledglings were the strangest-looking chickens either

Astrid or Siegfred had ever seen. Soon they grew long and lank and made the queerest sounds in their throats as they followed after the old gray goose.

One thing they would not do — they would not go swimming no matter how the gray goose urged. Finally she gave up trying. She would swim out in the water with her own babies, while her two Vinland children stayed cheerfully on the shore, scratching about in the dirt and eating wild seeds from the bushes.

Astrid and Siegfred were sorry they could not call Olaf to look at them. But Olaf had gone with some of the men to a place near Vinland which the Vikings called Hop. In Hop they would gather wild grapes and grains which grew plentifully there. The wild grapes were dried, and they tasted very good to the Vikings.

Several months passed before Olaf returned to Vinland. When they saw his boat coming, the children ran to the seashore and began jumping up and down and waving their hands in their eagerness to talk to him.

"What on earth has happened?" he asked when he landed and Siegfred grabbed one hand, Astrid the other.

"I've found it, I've found it!" said Astrid, laughing.

"Found what?"

"The answer to the riddle. Now we know when a pet hen is not a hen. Come, and we will show you," said Astrid.

404

The pair of children went dancing along beside Olaf until they came to the lake. There was the old gray goose swimming with her young ones, who were almost grown now. But on the shore two of the strangest birds Olaf had ever seen were wandering contentedly about.

Astrid made a little gobbling noise in her throat and these two strange birds came running over to her on long black legs. Then from the little pouch that hung at her waist, Astrid held out a handful of wild grain. The birds ate the seeds from her outstretched hand.

After they were all gone, one of the birds spread wide a bronze tail, shaped like a fan. The bronze fan had a border of white all along the edge.

"There is the answer, Olaf," said Astrid. "A pet hen is not a hen when it is a Vinland bird. See!" As Astrid walked up the path, the two strange birds followed at her heels. Wherever Astrid went, the Vinland birds would immediately try to go.

"Yes," Olaf said, "you have found the answer. When one leaves the thing one loves in the old home, one finds other things in the new."

Neither Olaf nor Astrid nor Siegfred could know that four centuries were to pass before Europeans would know much about the birds like those which Siegfred's old gray goose had hatched. Then Europeans were to call them turkeys, which was a strange name to give them. They might better have been called Vinland birds.

As for Astrid, she loved her great Vinland birds just as much as she had loved the little black hen. And after two years, when the Vikings loaded their dragon boats once more and sailed back to Greenland, I am very sure she took the strange birds with her.

The Vikings in Greenland must have been greatly astonished to see the biggest one spread his bronze, white-tipped tail and say, "Gobble, gobble, gobble!"

Catherine Cate Coblentz

FOR CHRISTMAS

Now not a window small or big
But wears a wreath or holly sprig;
Nor any shop too poor to show
Its spray of pine or mistletoe.
Now city airs are spicy-sweet
With Christmas trees along each street,
Green spruce and fir whose boughs will hold
Their tinseled balls and fruits of gold.
Now postmen pass in threes and fours
Like bent, blue-coated Santa Claus.
Now people hurry to and fro
With little girls and boys in tow,
And not a child but keeps some trace
Of Christmas secrets in his face.

Rachel Field

THE CHRISTMAS PROMISE

WHEN the Christ Child was born in Bethlehem of Judea, long years ago, three kings rode out of the East on their camels, bearing gifts to Him. They followed the star until at last they came to the manger where He lay, a little, new-born baby. Kneeling down, they put their gifts beside Him — gold, frankincense, and myrrh. They kissed the hem of the little white mantle that He wore, and blessed Him. Then the kings rode away to the East again, but before they went they whispered a promise to the Christ Child.

The promise? You shall hear it as the kings gave it to the Christ Child, long years ago.

"As long as there be children on the earth, on every Christmas Eve we three kings shall ride on camels, even as we rode to Thee this night. And even as we bore Thee gifts, so shall we bear gifts to every child in memory of Thee — Thou holy Babe of Bethlehem!"

In Spain they have remembered what the Christmas kings promised, and when Christmas Eve comes, each child puts his shoe between the gratings of the window so that the kings may know a child is in that house and leave a gift.

Often the shoe is filled with grass for the camels, and a plate of dates and figs is left beside it, for the children know the kings have far to go and may be hungry.

At day's end, bands of children march out of the city gates, going to meet the kings. But it always grows dark before the kings come. The children are afraid upon the lonely road and hurry back to their homes, where their mothers hear them say one prayer to the Christ Child, and then put them to bed to dream of the Christmas kings.

Long, long ago there lived in Spain, in the crowded part of a great city, an old woman called Doña Josefa. The street in which she lived was little and narrow, so narrow that if you leaned out of the window of Doña Josefa's house, you could touch with your fingertips the house across the way. When you looked above your head the sky seemed but a string of blue, tying the houses all together. The sun never found its way into this little street.

The people who lived here were very poor, as you may guess. Doña Josefa was poor, too. But in one thing she was very rich — she knew more stories than there were feast-days in the year, and that is a great many in Spain. Whenever there came a moment free from work, when Doña Josefa had no water to fetch from the public well, nor gold to stitch upon the altar cloth for the Church of Santa Maria del Rosario, then she would run out of her house into the street and call, "Children, children, come quickly! Here is a story waiting for you."

And the children would come flying like the gray doves when corn is thrown for them in the Plaza. Ah, how many children there were in that little street! Manuel and Rosita were always among them. They had no father, and their mother, to make their living, stood all day on the banks of the river outside the city, washing clothes.

When Doña Josefa had called the children from all the doorways and the dark corners, she would sit down in the middle of the street and gather them about her. This was safe because the street was far too narrow to allow a horse or wagon to pass through. Sometimes a donkey would slowly pick its way along, or a stupid goat come searching for things to eat, but that was all.

It happened on the day before Christmas that Doña Josefa had finished her work and sat, as usual, with the children about her.

"Today you shall have a Christmas story," she said. Then she told them of the three kings and the promise they had made the Christ Child.

"Do the kings bring presents to the children now?" Manuel asked.

Doña Josefa nodded her head.

"Yes."

"Then why have they never left us one? The three

kings never pass this street on Christmas Eve. Why is it,
Doña Josefa?"

"Perhaps it is because we have no shoes to hold their
gifts," said Rosita.

It is true that the poor children of Spain go barefooted,
and often never have a pair of shoes till they grow up.

"I know why it is the kings bring no gifts to us," said Manuel. "See, the street is too small. Their camels could not pass between the doorsteps here. The kings must ride where the streets are broad and smooth and clean, where their long mantles will not be soiled and torn, and the camels will not stumble. It is the children in the great streets, the children of the rich, who find presents in their shoes on Christmas morning. Is it not so, Doña Josefa?"

And Rosita cried, "Does Manuel speak true — is it only the children of the rich?"

"Ah, my little one, it should not be so! When the promise was given to the Christ Child there in Bethlehem, they said, 'to every child.' Yes, every little child."

"But it is not strange they should forget us here," Manuel insisted. "The little street is hidden in the shadow of the great ones."

Then Rosita said, clasping her hands together with great eagerness, "I am sure it is because we have no shoes to place between the gratings! That is why they never stop. Perhaps Enrique, the cobbler, would lend us the shoes he is mending, just for one night. If we had shoes the kings would surely see that there are little children in the street, and leave a gift for each of us. Come, let us ask Enrique!"

"What a blessed thought!" cried all the children. And like the flock of gray doves they swept down the street to the farthest end, where Enrique hammered and stitched away all day on the shoes of the rich children.

Manuel stayed behind with Doña Josefa. When the last pair of little brown feet had disappeared inside the cobbler's shop he said, softly, "If someone could go out and meet the kings to tell them how the children on this little street have never had a Christmas gift, do you think they might ride in this direction tonight?"

Doña Josefa shook her head doubtfully.

"If that were possible! But never have I heard of anyone who met the kings on Christmas Eve."

All day in the city people hurried to and fro. In the great streets flags were waving from the housetops, and green wreaths or garlands of sweet-smelling flowers hung above the open doorways and in the windows. Sweetmeat-sellers were crying their wares, and the Keeper-of-the-City lighted flaming torches to hang upon the gates and city walls.

Merry-making and gladness were everywhere, for not only was this Christmas Eve, but the King of Spain was coming to keep his holiday within the city. Some whispered that he was riding from the north, and that with him rode his cousins, the two kings of France and Lombardy, and that with them were a great following of nobles, knights, and minstrels. Others said the kings rode all alone by their own wish.

413

As the sun was turning the cathedral spires to shafts of gold, bands of children, hand in hand, marched out of the city. They took the road that led toward the setting sun, thinking it was the east, and said among themselves, "See, yonder is the way the kings will ride."

"I have brought a basket of figs," cried one.

"I have dates," cried another.

"And I," cried a third, "I have brought a sack of sweet oranges, because they are so cooling."

Thus each in turn showed some small gift that he was bringing for the kings. And while they chatted together, one child began to sing the sweet Nativity Hymn. In a moment others joined until the soft night air rang with their happy voices.

"Unto us a Child is born,
        Unto us a gift is given.
Hail with holiness the morn,
        Kneel before the Prince of Heaven.

"Blessed be this day of birth,
        God hath given His Son to earth.
Jesu, Jesu, Nene Jesu,
        Hallelujah!"

Behind the little hills the sun went down leaving a million sparks of light upon the road.

"Yonder come the kings!" the children cried, when they saw this sunset light. "See the splendor of their shining crowns, and how the jewels sparkle on their mantles! They may be angry if they find us out so late. Come, let us run home before they see us."

The children turned. Back to the city gates they ran, back to their homes, to the mothers watching for them, and their own white beds ready for them.

But one they left behind them on the road — a little, barefoot boy whose name was Manuel. He watched until the children had disappeared within the gates, and then he turned again toward the setting sun.

"I have no gifts for the kings," he thought. "But there is fresh green grass beside the way that I can gather for the camels."

He stooped, pulled his hands full, and stuffed it in the front of the little blue shirt that he wore. He followed the road for a long way until heavy sleep came to his eyes.

"How still it is upon the road! God has blown out His light and soon it will be dark. I wish I were with the others, safe within the city, for the dark is full of fearsome things when one is all alone. Mamma will be coming home soon and bringing supper for Rosita and me. I hope Rosita will not forget the little prayer I told her always to say. My feet hurt with the many stones. The night wind blows so cold. I am weary and my feet stumble with me. O Baby

Jesus, listen! I also make the prayer: 'Send the three kings before Manuel is too weary and afraid!'"

A few more steps he took upon the road, and then, as a reed is blown down by the wind, Manuel slowly sank upon the ground, fast asleep.

How long he slept I cannot tell you, but a hand on his shoulder wakened him. Quickly he opened his eyes, wondering, and saw — yes, he saw the three kings! Tall and splendid they looked in the starlight, their mantles shimmering with golden threads. One stood above Manuel, asking what he did upon the road at that late hour.

Manuel rose to his feet, thrusting his hand inside the shirt for the grass he had gathered.

"It is for the camels, señor. I have no other gift. But you — you ride horses this Christmas Eve!"

"Yes, we ride horses. What is that to you?"

"Pardon, señores, nothing. The three kings can ride horses if they wish, only — we were told you rode on camels from the East."

"What does the child want?" The voice was kind, but it sounded impatient, as though the one who spoke had work waiting to be done and was anxious to be about it.

Manuel heard and felt all this, wondering, "What if

there is not time for them to come, or gifts enough!" He laid an eager, pleading hand on one king's mantle.

"I can hold the horses if you will come this once. It is a little street and hard to find, señores. I thought perhaps you would leave a present — just one little present for the children there. You told the Christ Child you would give to every child. Don't you remember? There are many of us who have never had a gift — a Christmas gift."

"Do you know who we are?"

Manuel answered joyfully, "Oh, yes, Excellencies! You are the Three Christmas Kings, riding from Bethlehem."

The kings looked at one another.

"We are indeed three kings," said the one with the kind voice.

"You will come with me to our street?" begged Manuel.

The kings spoke with one accord, "We will come."

One lifted Manuel on his horse, and silently they rode into the city. The Keeper slept at the gates. The streets were empty. On past the houses that were gar-landed they went unseen; and on through the great streets until they came to the little street at last. The kings dis-mounted. They gave their bridles into Manuel's hand, and then, gathering up their precious mantles of silk and rich brocade, they passed down the little street. With eyes that scarce believed what they saw, Manuel watched them go from house to house. He saw them stop and feel

418

for the shoes between the gratings — the shoes the children had borrowed from Enrique, the cobbler — and saw them fill each one with shining gold pieces.

In the morning Manuel told the story to the children as they went from shop to little shop to spend some of the precious gold pieces for toys and candy and sugared cakes. They bought a gift for Doña Josefa, too — a little figure of the Holy Mother with the Christ Child in her arms.

And so the promise made in Bethlehem was kept again. For many, many years, long after Manuel was grown and had children of his own, the kings remembered the little street, and brought their gifts there every Christmas Eve.

Ruth Sawyer

THE NEW YEAR

Who comes dancing over the snow,
  His soft little feet all bare and rosy?
Open the door, though the wild winds blow,
  Take the child in and make him cozy.
Take him in and hold him dear;
  He is the wonderful glad New Year.

Dinah M. M. Craik

419

SAINT VALENTINE

I'm sure I don't know who he was,
The saint whose name was Valentine;
Nor what he could have done to cause
A holiday like yours and mine.

But this I do know: he was kind,
And people loved him near and far;
So when he died they had a mind
To keep him in the calendar.

He must have been a man who knew
A lot of secrets everywhere
But never told — just laughed, and drew
A frilly pattern in the air.

And when at dusk he walked the town,
Shy lovers curtsied as he passed,
And children, as the dark came down,
Ran to his hand and held it fast.

Eunice Tietjens

420

THE LAST SNAKE

S AINT PATRICK sat down under the shade of an old apple tree. It was a warm day and he was feeling hot and tired. Getting rid of all the snakes in Ireland was not so easy as some people supposed and Saint Patrick needed a rest.

Some of the snakes he had driven into the sea, some he had driven into the rocks, and some he had magicked away entirely. It was easy enough when the snakes wanted to be driven into the sea or wanted to be driven into the rocks. But sometimes they didn't. Then Saint Patrick had to beg and scold until they minded, and that was what made him hot and tired.

He sat down under the apple tree, and pretty soon he lay back in the soft grass that is so green it makes people call Ireland the "Emerald Isle." The grass was cool, and for a few moments Saint Patrick was at peace. For a few moments, but not for long. Soon a small black spider ran out of the grass and up Saint Patrick's neck. It tickled him.

Saint Patrick slapped off the spider and settled back to his rest. He shut his eyes and thought how peaceful Ireland would now be without the snakes. Just then there

was a buzzing in Saint Patrick's ear. It wasn't a loud buzzing, but neither was it a peaceful buzzing, and Saint Patrick
sat up again and slapped. It was a mosquito, and Saint
Patrick didn't like mosquitoes a bit.

When he was rid of the mosquito, Saint Patrick lay down again, but he had hardly stretched himself out before he felt another thing crawling up the side of his face. This time it was a shiny biting bug and Saint Patrick shook it off very quickly.

"Begone!" he said. "And have done with you. Can't a man have his rest?"

But it seemed a man couldn't, for soon there was the same black bug or another one like it climbing up the back of Saint Patrick's head. This time Saint Patrick sat up very straight and he was as cross as a saint can well be.

"Will you be gone," he said, "or shall I never be rid of you? Surely if I free Ireland of snakes, there should be someone to rid me, once and for all, of these bothersome, biting creatures."

And with that Saint Patrick settled back for the third and last time. This time he really went to sleep and not one creeping creature bothered him.

He slept and he slept and at last, when he woke up, he felt better. Now Saint Patrick was rested and cool and ready to go about his business. He sat up and stretched, and stood up and stretched, and he was just starting out on his way when he looked down and saw something that stopped him. There at his feet was the smallest, brownest snake in all Ireland.

"Well," said Saint Patrick, and now he was so well

rested that he couldn't be cross. "It's yourself has the nerve. Haven't you heard I'm sending all the snakes out of Ireland?"

The small brown snake said nothing, nor did it look the saint in the face. Instead, it wriggled quickly forward. Saint Patrick looked to see where it was wriggling and there, right in front of the snake on the open part of Saint Patrick's sandal, was another small black spider. The Saint stared and the snake wriggled. The next instant its small sharp tongue darted out and the spider was gone! It was gone without a shadow of a doubt, for the snake had eaten it.

As the snake glided off to a small sunny patch in the grass, Saint Patrick just looked at it.

"Well," he said, and his voice still sounded fresh and rested. "So that's how it is! I rid Ireland of the snakes, and you rid Patrick of biting things."

He stood and frowned, looking down at the snake. It was a very small snake and it never looked at Saint Patrick with its bright, unwinking eyes. Instead, it just lay sunning itself. Whenever a bug or a fly, or any kind of a creeping, crawling creature passed near by, out shot the snake's sharp little tongue and the creeping, crawling creature was no more.

"I could drive you into the sea," said Saint Patrick, "or drive you into the rock, or magic you away entirely."

424

Still the snake said nothing, but lay coiled in the warm sunshine. "Or since you got me my rest," the Saint went on, "I could let you have yours."

Still the snake said nothing but it gobbled up a mosquito with a little snap.

"That's just what I'll do," said Saint Patrick and with that he pointed at the snake just as though he were going to magic it away entirely.

But the small brown snake didn't magic away. It lay quite still and as it lay it grew harder and harder to see. It was no longer brown, no, nor nearly brown. It was a bright emerald green, just the color of the grass of Ireland.

"There!" said Saint Patrick, when he could hardly see the snake himself. "There, now you are safe, you and all your kind. Other birds and beasts cannot see you. And as for man, surely no one would harm a little snake that is green as Ireland itself and spends its days adding to the peace of mankind."

Lavinia Davis

425

GLOSSARY

The glossary gives 280 selected words appearing in *Merry Hearts and Bold*. The meaning of each word is explained in a definition which fits the way it is used on the page given. In this glossary, as in a dictionary, there are guide words at the top of each page. The word at the left top is the first word listed on that page, and the word at the right top is the last word listed on the same page. The words in the list are divided into syllables and the accents are marked. A heavy mark ′ is placed after a syllable with a primary or strong accent. A lighter mark ′ is placed after a syllable with a secondary or lighter accent. The pronunciation is given in parentheses after each word. Diacritical marks are used with some of the letters in the pronunciation of a word. These marks tell the sounds the letters have in the word. The list below and the words at the bottom of the right-hand pages show which sound of a letter each diacritical mark means.

ā	as in āte	ē	as in bē	ō	as in hōpe
ă	as in ăm	ĕ	as in mĕt	ŏ	as in hŏt
â	as in câre	ẹ	as in hẹre	ô	as in lôrd
ȧ	as in ȧsk	ẽ	as in makẽr		
a	as in about			ū	as in ūse
ä	as in fär	ī	as in bīte	ŭ	as in ŭp
		ĭ	as in bĭt	û	as in bûrn

th	as in thin	o͞o	as in fo͞od
th	as in then	o͝o	as in fo͝ot
tū	as in pictūre	ou	as in out

A

ab′bot (ăb′ŭt), the head of a monastery. (p. 297)

A chil′les (a kĭl′ēz), a Greek hero. (p. 122)

A′dri at′ic (ā′drĭ ăt′ĭk), the sea east of Italy. (p. 302)

Ae ne′as (ē nē′ås), a prince of ancient Troy. (p. 297)

af firm′ (a fûrm′), say firmly; declare to be true. (p. 382)

Af ghan′is tan (ăf găn′ĭ stăn), a country in southern Asia, north of India. (p. 323)

al′der men (ôl′dẽr mĕn), public officers. (p. 140)

am′ber (ăm′bẽr), yellow or yellowish-brown. (p. 35)

a miss′ (a mĭs′), wrong; not the way it should be. (p. 241)

am′u let (ăm′ū lĕt), something worn as a charm. (p. 293)

426

A'mund sen, Roald (ä'mŭn-
sĕn, rō'ȧld), discoverer of the
South Pole, 1911. (p. 348)
a poth'e car'y (ȧ pŏth'ē kĕr'ĭ),
a druggist. (p. 260)
ap pren'tice (ȧ prĕn'tĭs), a person who serves a master in
learning a trade or an art. (p.
302)
arch'er y (är'chĕr ĭ), shooting
with bow and arrows. (p. 44)
Ar'is tot'le (är'ĭs tŏt'l), a famous Greek teacher. (p. 121)
as bes'tos (ăs bĕs'tŏs), a mineral
substance that will not burn.
(p. 325)
as sured' (ȧ shoŏrd'), told posi-
tively. (p. 25)
as tron'o my (ăs trŏn'ō mĭ), the
study of the stars. (p. 374)
au'di ence (ô'dĭ ĕns), a chance
to be heard. (p. 214)

B

ba'bel (bā'bĕl), a confusion of
sounds. (p. 390)
bal'lad (băl'ăd), a song or poem
that tells a story. (p. 309)
bar bar'ic (bär băr'ĭk), rude,
coarse; not civilized. (p. 326)
Bar'bar y (bär'bȧ rĭ), old name
for the countries in northern
Africa west of Egypt on the
Mediterranean Sea. (p. 134)

barges (bärjez), roomy boats,
usually flat-bottomed, used
chiefly on rivers and canals.
(p. 339)
ba zaar' (bȧ zär'), a market-
place. (p. 93)
Ber'bers (bûr'bĕrz), a people in
northern Africa. (p. 151)
blank'ly (blăngk'lĭ), without expression. (p. 298)
Bo he'mi a (bō hē'mĭ ȧ), a district of central Europe, at one
time a kingdom. (p. 312)
boul'der (bōl'dĕr), a large rock,
rounded or worn by water and
weather. (p. 158)
bow'sprit (bou'sprĭt), the pole
or spar that projects from the
bow or front of a ship. (p.
238)
breech cloths (brēch klŏthz),
cloths fastened about the hips.
(p. 181)
Brit'ta ny (brĭt'ȧ nĭ), a district
in northwestern France. (p.
289)
bro cade' (brō kād'), a fine cloth
woven with a raised design.
(p. 180)
Bruns'wick (brŭnz'wĭk), a district in the central part of Germany. (p. 51)
Bryant, William Cullen. See
William Cullen Bryant.

āte, ăm, câre, ȧsk, ȧbout, fär, bē, mĕt, hẽre, makẽr, bīte, bĭt, hōpe,
hŏt, lôrd, ūse, ŭp, bûrn, thin, then, pictūre, foŏd, foŏt, out

Bu ceph'a lus (bū sĕf'ȧ lŭs), the famous war horse of Alexander the Great. (p. 121)

C

Cabot, John. See **John Cabot.**

cal'a bash (kăl'ȧ băsh), the dried shell of fruit like a squash, used as a basket. (p. 187)

Cam'er oons' (kăm'ēr ōōnz'), a region in west-central Africa. (p. 185)

cam'phor (kăm'fēr), a white substance with a strong odor and a bitter taste. (p. 329)

Ca nar'i ans (kȧ när'ĭ ănz), people who live in the Canary Islands. (p. 384)

can teen' (kăn tēn'), a small container used for carrying water. (p. 81)

Ca thay' (kȧ thā'), an old name for China. (p. 321)

cen'tu ries (sĕn'tū rĭz), hundreds of years. (p. 298)

cha let' (shă lā'), a Swiss cottage. (p. 101)

cham'ber lain (chăm'bēr lĭn), an officer who manages the household of a king. (p. 247)

chant'ed (chȧnt'ĕd), sang slowly. (p. 320)

char'ac ter (kăr'ăk tēr), one of the persons of a play. (p. 332)

Char'le magne (shär'lĕ măn), Charles the Great. (p. 289)

chinked (chĭngkt), filled up. (p. 289)

Chlo til'de (klō tĭl'dȧ), a French noblewoman. (p. 290)

civ'i lized (sĭv'ĭ līzd), a highly developed way of living. (p. 326)

cob'ble stones' (kŏb'l stōnz'), rounded stones used for paving a street. (p. 90)

com mo'tion (kŏ mō'shŭn), a noisy moving about of people. (p. 147)

con firmed' (kŏn fûrmd'), made certain; proved by an example or results obtained. (p. 328)

con'ger eel (kŏng'gēr ēl), a large eel, or snakelike fish, that lives in the ocean and is caught for food. (p. 200)

Con'stan ti no'ple (kŏn'stăn tĭ nō'p'l), a large city in Turkey, now called Istanbul. (p. 322)

con'tra ry (kŏn'trēr ĭ), unfavorable. (p. 331)

con vert'ed (kŏn vûr'tĕd), caused to change from unbelief to faith. (p. 384)

coun'ci lors (koun'sĭ lērz), men who give advice. (p. 219)

coun'ter-at tack' (koun'tēr ȧtăk'), an attack made against an enemy who has already attacked. (p. 151)

count'ing-house (kount'ĭnghous'), an office where business is carried on. (p. 131)

428

Cro'-Ma'gnon' (krō'mȧ'nyôn'), men supposed to be the ancestors of modern man. (p. 157)

Cru sade' (krōō sād'), an attempt by Christian armies to recover the Holy Land from the Mohammedans. (p. 301)

Cu chu'lain (kōō hōō'lĭn), a legendary Irish hero. (p. 231)

cur'ried (kûr'ĭd), brushed with a metal comb. (p. 91)

D

Dan'ube (dăn'ūb), a large river that flows into the Black Sea. (p. 312)

dazed (dāzd), stunned. (p. 311)

de scent' (dē sĕnt'), the downward trail. (p. 107)

dic'tate (dĭk'tāt), to tell or utter so that another may write down. (p. 332)

dis as'ter (dĭ zȧs'tēr), an event such as flood, fire, or shipwreck which brings distress to many people. (p. 28)

Do'ña (dō'nyä), madam; a Spanish title of respect. (p. 409)

dor'sal fin (dôr'săl), the fin on the back of a fish. (p. 201)

dou'blet (dŭb'lĭt), a man's close-fitting jacket. Men wore doublet and hose in Europe from 1400 to 1600. (p. 382)

Dov er fjeld' (dŏv rĕ fyăl'), the high central land of Norway. (p. 351)

draw'bridge (drô'brĭj), a bridge that can be lifted up or drawn aside. (p. 289)

dunes (dūnz), mounds of sand piled up by the wind. (p. 150)

E

em bar'rassed (ĕm băr'ȧst), disturbed; bothered. (p. 12)

e mer'gen cy kit (ē mûr'jĕn sĭ), a collection of medicines, etc., for use in case of accident. (p. 82)

En ri'que (ĕn rē'kā), *Henry* in Spanish. (p. 412)

en'vi ous (ĕn'vĭ ŭs), wishing to have something that belongs to someone else. (p. 91)

en'voys (ĕn'voiz), persons sent on business by a king or government. (p. 290)

e ro'sion (ē rō'zhŭn), wearing away of the soil. (p. 79)

es cort' (ĕs kôrt'), to go with as a protection, guide, or mark of honor. (p. 330)

Es co ve'do, Ro dri'go de (ĕs-kō vĕ'thō, rō thrē'gō dĕ), secretary of Columbus's fleet. (p. 383)

āte, ăm, câre, ȧsk, ȧbout, fär, bē, mĕt, hẽre, makẽr, bīte, bĭt, hōpe, hŏt, lôrd, ūse, ŭp, bûrn, thin, then, pictu̱re, fōod, fŏot, out

eu′ca lyp′tus (ū′kȧ lĭp′tŭs), a tree that grows in Australia and California. (p. 79)

Ex′cel len cies (ĕk′sĕ lĕn sĭz), a title of respect. (p. 418)

ex per′i ment (ĕks pĕr′ĭ mĕnt), a trial or test to find out something. (p. 341)

F

fare (fâr), food. Hard fare is poor or little food. (p. 127)

Far′ra gut (făr′ȧ gŭt), David G., a Northern admiral in the War Between the States. (p. 374)

fear′some (fēr′sŭm), causing fright. (p. 415)

fiend (fēnd), a cruel person. (p. 395)

fiord (fyôrd), a narrow inlet of the sea between high, steep rocks. (p. 60)

flag′stones′ (flăg′stonz′), large, flat paving stones. (p. 69)

Flan′ders (flăn′dĕrz), a district in Europe, now a part of Belgium and France. (p. 50)

fledg′lings (flĕj′lĭngz), young birds. (p. 403)

fore′cas tle (fōk′s'l), that part of the upper deck of a vessel forward of the foremast or the mast nearest the bow. (p. 382)

fore see′ing (fōr sē′ing), knowing ahead of time. (p. 123)

fort′night (fôrt′nīt), two weeks. (p. 346)

frank′in cense (frăngk′ĭn sĕns), a gum which gives off a sweet smell when burned. (p. 408)

Franks (frăngks), people whose kingdom included a large part of what is now Germany, France, Belgium, Holland. (p. 289)

G

Gains′bor ough (gānz′bŭ rŭ), Thomas, an English portrait painter. (p. 333)

gal′ley (găl′ĭ), a ship moved by oars or by oars and sails. (p. 332)

ge om′e try (jē ŏm′ĕ trĭ), the measurement of squares, circles, angles, etc. (p. 374)

gill-slits (gĭl-slĭts), openings through which a fish breathes under water. (p. 205)

glare (glâr), a fierce or piercing look. (p. 59)

Gold Coast (gōld cōst), a British colony on the West African coast. (p. 185)

Gou′da (gou′dȧ), a city in South Holland. (p. 169)

Gua′na ha′ni (gwä′nä hä′nē), the island on which Columbus first landed. (p. 383)

guil′ders (gĭl′dĕrz), Dutch coins worth about forty cents each in U. S. money. (p. 169)

Guin′ea (gĭn′ĭ), a coast region in West Africa. (p. 376)

H

hal′le lu′jah (hăl′ē lōō′yạ), an exclamation meaning "Praise ye the Lord!" (p. 414)

har poon′ (här pōōn′), a spear with a rope tied to it. (p. 196)

hea′then (hē′t̶h̶ĕn), member of a people that does not accept the God of the Bible. (p. 297)

herbs (ûrbz), plants with leaves that are used for food, flavoring, or medicine. (p. 403)

hilt (hĭlt), handle. (p. 239)

Ho′dja (hō′jạ), a Turkish title meaning teacher-priest. (p. 44)

hove (hōv), brought to a standstill by heading into the wind with headsails aback. (p. 383)

I

i′dle (ī′d'l), inactive, useless. (p. 323)

im′age (ĭm′ĭj), a likeness. (p. 336)

im pres′sions (ĭm prĕsh′ŭnz), definite remembrances, beliefs, or opinions. (p. 324)

in gen′ious (ĭn jēn′yŭs), skillful at making or inventing. (p. 385)

in spec′tors (ĭn spĕk′tērz), men who examine things to see if they are all right. (p. 326)

in′ spi ra′tion (ĭn′spĭ rā′shŭn), sudden, very clear idea as to what to do. (p. 153)

J

Jacques (zhȧk), *Jack* in French. (p. 302)

jade (jād), green gem stones. (p. 13)

Ja′pheth (jā′fĕth), Noah's youngest son. (p. 36)

jaun′ty (jòn′tĭ), having a free and easy manner. (p. 47)

Je su′, Ne′ne Je su′ (hā sōō′, nĕ′nĕ), meaning "Jesus, little Jesus." (p. 414)

John Ca′bot (jŏn kăb′ŭt), Venetian navigator in service of England. Discovered continent of North America in 1497. (p. 377)

Jo se′fa (hō sĕf′ȧ), *Josephine* in Spanish (p. 409)

Jo′seph Mal′lord Wil′liam Tur′ner (jō′zĕf măl′ērd wĭl′yạm tûr′nēr), one of England's greatest landscape painters. (p. 338)

K

khan (kän), a Tartar title meaning lord or prince (p. 322)

knoll (nōl), a low, rounded hill. (p. 288)

āte, ăm, câre, ȧsk, ạbout, fär, bē, mĕt, hẹre, makēr, bīte, bĭt, hōpe, hŏt, lòrd, ūse, ŭp, bùrn, thin, t̶h̶e̶n̶, pictụre, fōōd, fŏŏt, out

431

Knu′bel (k′nōō′b′l), a Swiss postmaster. (p. 109)

ko′la nut (kō′lȧ), a small brown nut. (p. 181)

kro′ner (krō′nĕr), Scandinavian gold monetary units; so called in Denmark and Norway. (p. 59)

L

lad′ing (lād′ĭng), cargo; freight. A bill of lading is a list of the goods shipped. (p. 137)

la goon′ (lȧ gōōn′), the shallow pond or lake within a ring-shaped coral island. (p. 195)

La-mei′ (lä-mā′), daughter of the Magistrate. (p. 12)

land′skips (lănd′skĭps), landscapes; paintings or drawings of natural scenes. (p. 337)

lank (lăngk), thin. (p. 404)

Las Ca′sas, Bar′thol′o mew, (läs kä′säs, bär′thŏl′ō mū), one of Columbus's companions on his famous voyage. (p. 381)

launched (lôncht), set afloat, ready to start off. (p. 148)

lee side (lē sīd), the side protected from the wind. (p. 358)

lib′er al-mind′ed (lĭb′ĕr ăl-mīnd′ĕd), generous; having a readiness to give. (p. 331)

Lis′bon (lĭz′bŭn), capital of Portugal. (p. 376)

Lom′bar dy (lŏm′bĕr dĭ), a region in northern Italy. (p. 413)

lo′tus (lō′tŭs), a large water lily that grows in Egypt and Asia. (p. 5)

Lu ca′yos (lōō kä′yōs), the Bahama Islands. (p. 383)

lurked (lûrkt), stayed in or about a place secretly. (p. 375)

M

Mac′e do′ni a (măs′ē dō′nĭ ȧ), name of an old country just north of Greece. (p. 120)

Mag′de burg (măg′dē bûrg), a city in Germany. (p. 54)

ma gen′ta (mȧ jĕn′tȧ), a reddish-purple color. (p. 181)

man′gled (măng′g′ld), badly cut or torn. (p. 261)

man′goes (măng′gōz), fruit of a tree that grows in hot countries. (p. 186)

man′u script (măn′ū skrĭpt), the handwritten sheets of a book. (p. 297)

mar′a ve′dis (măr′ȧ vā′dĭs), Spanish copper coin units, introduced by Ferdinand and Isabella. (p. 382)

Mel′bourne (mĕl′bērn), a large city on the southern coast of Australia. (p. 78)

Me′nes (mē′nēz), an Egyptian boy. (p. 280)

min′strels (mĭn′strĕlz), singers or musicians who wandered about from place to place. (p. 413)

mon′as ter′ies (mŏn′ăs tĕr′ĭz), the homes of monks. (p. 291)

Mon go′li an (mŏng gō′li ăn), of Mongolia, a vast region north of China. (p. 44)

Moors (mŏŏrz), people of northern Africa related to the Arabs. (p. 134)

Mo′zart (mō′tsärt), famous Austrian composer. (p. 375)

mum′mi fied (mŭm′ĭ fīd), preserved from decay. (p. 329)

mu ni′tions (mū nĭsh′ŭnz), materials used in war. (p. 329)

myrrh (mûr), a fragrant, bitter gummy substance. (p. 408)

N

Nasr′-ed-Din (näsr′-ĕd-dĭn), a Turkish teacher-priest. (p. 44)

nav′i ga′tion (năv′ĭ gā′shŭn), the science or art of planning a ship's course. (p. 374)

Nor′man dy (nôr′măn dĭ), a region in France bordering the English Channel. (p. 301)

O

o blig′ing (ō blīj′ĭng), willing to do things for others. (p. 233)

o′gres (ō′gĕrz), ugly giants who were cruel. (p. 388)

ore (ōr), rock, sand, or dirt containing metal. (p. 355)

P

pag′eants (păj′ĕnts), public entertainments representing scenes from history or legend. (p. 332)

pan da′nus (păn dā′nŭs), tropical, palm-like plant. (p. 196)

pangs (păngz), sudden feelings of pain. (p. 324)

par′a keets (păr′ă kēts), small, long-tailed parrots. (p. 202)

parch′ment (pärch′mĕnt), the skin of sheep or goats, so prepared that it can be written on, like paper. (p. 21)

pa trol′ling (pă trōl′ĭng), keeping watch. (p. 325)

pa′tron saint (pā′trŭn sānt), the saint who helps, guards, or protects one. (p. 308)

ped′es tals (pĕd′ĕs tălz), bases or supports on which something stands or sits. (p. 176)

pe′o ny (pē′ō nĭ), a plant having large, showy flowers. (p. 9)

per sist′ent (pĕr sĭs′tĕnt), having enduring or staying qualities in spite of hardship or disapproval. (p. 327)

phan′tom (făn′tŭm), seeming to be, but not actually, real. (p. 388)

Phi lon′i cus (fĭ lŏn′ĭ kŭs), a horse dealer. (p. 121)

āte, ăm, câre, ȧsk, ȧbout, fär, bē, mĕt, hẹre, makēr, bīte, bĭt, hōpe, hŏt, lôrd, ūse, ŭp, bûrn, thin, then, pictŭre, fŏŏd, fŏŏt, out

phos′pho rus (fŏs′fō rŭs), a substance which glows with light in the dark. (p. 204)

pil′lo ries (pĭl′ō rĭz), instruments of punishment, consisting of wooden frames with holes in which a person's head and hands could be locked. (p. 324)

Pin zon′, Mar tin′ A lon′zo (pēn thōn′, mär tēn′ ä lŏn′zō), 1440(?)–1493, captain of the *Pinta*. (p. 383)

Pin zon′, Vin′cent Ya′nez (pēn-thōn′, vĭn′sĕnt yä′nĕth), 1460(?)–1524, captain of the *Niña* (nē′nyä). (p. 383)

pomp′ous (pŏmp′ŭs), with an enlarged feeling of importance. (p. 343)

poop (po͞op), a deck at the stern above the ordinary deck, often forming the roof of a cabin. (p. 382)

Po′rus (pō′rŭs), a prince of India, conquered by Alexander the Great. (p. 126)

Prague (präg), capital of Bohemia and Czechoslovakia. (p. 50)

prej′u dice (prĕj′o͝o dĭs), having one's mind set in one way, without regard for truth or reason. (p. 328)

pres′ence (prĕz′ĕns), place where a person is. (p. 22)

Priv′y Coun′cil (prĭv′ĭ koun′sĭl), group of men who give personal advice to a ruler. (p. 21)

pro mo′tion (prō mō′shŭn), advancement to a higher class or rank. (p. 329)

prowled (proul′d), wandered about slowly and secretly. (p. 141)

ptar′mi gan (tär′mĭ găn), medium-sized birds whose feathers are white in winter and gray, black, or brown in summer. (p. 348)

Pyr′e nees (pĭr′ē nēz), a chain of mountains between Spain and France. (p. 295)

Q

qual′i ties (kwŏl′ĭ tĭz), merits; things in a person's character that makes him what he is. (p. 326)

Queens′land (kwēnz′lănd), a large state in the northeastern part of Australia. (p. 78)

R

rare (râr), unusually good; of an uncommon quality. (p. 55)

re flect′ed (rē flĕk′tĕd), thought; considered. (p. 346)

re un′ion (rē ūn′yŭn), coming together again. (p. 151)

Roy′al A cad′e my (roi′ăl ȧ kăd′ē mĭ), a famous institute which maintains schools for teaching painting and other arts. (p. 347)

rug′ged (rŭg′ĕd), rough; sturdy; strong. (p. 378)

rumble (rŭm′b′l), a low, continuous sound. (p. 64)

ru′mor (roō′mēr), a story or statement talked of as news without any proof that it is true. (p. 328)

rush (rŭsh), a plant with round hollow stems that look something like the stems of grasses. (p. 381)

S

St. Nich′o las (sānt nĭk′ō lăs), patron saint of travelers and children whose anniversary is celebrated in Europe on December 6 as Saint Nicholas Day. (p. 54)

San′chez, Ro dri′go (sän′chĕth, rō thrē′gō), one of Columbus's companions. (p. 383)

sand′ pipers (sănd′ pīp ērz), small shore birds having long bills. (p. 381)

Sax′o ny (săk′sō nĭ), a state in southern Germany. (p. 50)

scene (sēn), picture, something viewed as a whole. (p. 324)

Schip pie ta′ro (shĭp i tä′rō), a brave dog. (p. 390)

scows (skouz), flat-bottomed, large boats, with square ends. (p. 8)

Scrip′tures (skrĭp′tūrz), books of the Bible. (p. 297)

scythes (sīthz), tools for mowing grass, consisting of a long, curved blade fastened to a long handle. (p. 251)

se dan′ chair (sē dăn′), a covered chair for carrying a person, borne on poles. (p. 9)

Se go′vi a (sā gō′vyä), a small city in Spain. (p. 383)

Sen e gal′ (sĕn ē gôl′), a colony in West Africa, bordering the Atlantic Ocean. (p. 185)

se ñor′, se ñor′es (sā nyôr′, sā-nyô′rās), Spanish title meaning *sir* or *mister*. (p. 416)

Ses′a me (sĕs′å mē), an East Indian plant, but in the phrase "Open Sesame" simply a part of a password. (p. 255)

shafts (shåfts), columns; slender monuments. (p. 414)

Shang′hai′ (shăng′hī′), a large city on the coast of China. (p. 14)

Shao′hing′ (zou′shĭng′), a city near Shanghai, China. (p. 3)

sher′iffs (shĕr′ĭfs), officers who see that laws are carried out. (p. 140)

shim′mer ing (shĭm′ēr ing), gleaming or shining faintly. (p. 416)

show′down (shō′doun), final test to determine which is master. (p. 175)

āte, ăm, câre, åsk, *a*bout, fär, bē, mĕt, hẽre, makēr, bīte, bĭt, hōpe, hŏt, lôrd, ūse, ŭp, bûrn, thin, then, pictūre, foōd, foŏt, out

siege (sēj), an attempt to gain possession. (p. 304)

silk-can'o pied (sĭlk-kăn'ō pĭd), having a covering of silk fastened to poles. (p. 8)

sil'ver smith' (sĭl'vĕr smĭth'), person who makes articles of silver. (p. 337)

sol'i tar'y (sŏl'ĭ tĕr'ĭ), lonely; unfrequented; away from people. (p. 337)

sov'er eigns (sŏv'ĕr ĭnz), persons vested with highest authority. (p. 383)

span (spăn), extend over. (p. 166)

spare (spâr), more than enough. (p. 321)

sprouts (sprouts), shoots of a plant. (p. 7)

squire (skwīr), a young man attending a knight. (p. 301)

stand'ard (stăn'dĕrd), flag, emblem, or symbol. (p. 383)

stat'ure (stăt'ūr), height. (p. 385)

stile (stīl), a set of steps used for getting over a fence. (p. 58)

stow it (stō), stop it. (p. 74)

Strat'ford-on-A'von (străt'fĕrd-ŏn-ā'vŭn), birthplace of William Shakespeare, the "other boy" mentioned. (p. 334)

stretch'er (strĕch'ĕr), a light frame of poles and strong canvas, for carrying sick or wounded persons. (p. 112)

strides (strīdz), long steps. (p. 318)

strum'ming (strŭm'ĭng), playing carelessly on a stringed musical instrument. (p. 305)

suf fo ca'tion (sŭf ō kā'shŭn), being unable to breathe. (p. 359)

sul'tan (sŭl'tăn), name of the ruler of old Turkey. (p. 94)

sun'-di'al (sŭn'-dī'ăl), an instrument to show the time of day by the position of a shadow cast by the sun. (p. 26)

sus pi'cious (sŭs pĭsh'ŭs), indicating doubt. (p. 82)

sweet'meat (swēt'mēt), candy or candied fruit. (p. 413)

T

Tar'ta ry (tär'tà rĭ), a district in both Asia and Europe extending from the Sea of Japan to the Dnieper River. (p. 330)

teak'wood (tēk'wŏŏd), a hard, brown wood. (p. 5)

tech nique' tĕk nēk'), the correct method. (p. 107)

tense (tĕns), tight; strained (p. 198)

Thames (tĕmz), the largest river in England. (p. 339)

Thebes (thēbz), ancient city near Athens, Greece. (p. 125)

ther'mos bottle (thûr'mŏs), a flask that keeps liquids hot or cold. (p. 110)

Thes'sa ly (thĕs'ȧ lĭ), a region in northern Greece, just south of Macedonia. (p. 120)

thongs (thŏngz), narrow strips of leather, used like strings or ropes for fastening. (p. 160)

tink'er (tĭngk'ẽr), a person who mends pots, pans, or other tinware. (p. 302)

tre men'dous (trē mĕn'dŭs), important; extraordinary. (p. 300)

tri'fles (trī'f'lz), things of little value or importance. (p. 35)

tri um'phant ly (trī ŭm'fănt lĭ), with joy because of success. (p. 265)

troll-folk (trōl-fōk), ugly dwarfs or giants, supposed to live in caves or hills. (p. 360)

trou'ba dours (troo'bȧ doorz), a group of traveling musicians, performers, or singers. (p. 302)

tru'ant (troo'ănt), one who stays away from school. (p. 334)

Tu'nis (tū'nĭs), a country in northern Africa, bordering on the Mediterranean Sea. (p. 375)

tur'baned (tûr'bănd), wearing hats made by winding a cloth round the head. (p. 89)

Turner, Joseph Mallord William. See **Joseph Mallord William Turner.**

U

U'len spie gel, Tyll (oo'lĕn-shpē gĕl, tĭl), a Flemish folk-hero. (p. 50)

Ul'ster (ŭl'stẽr) the northern part of Ireland. (p. 229)

V

Ven'ice (vĕn'ĭs), a city on the eastern coast of Italy. (p. 321)

ven'ture (vĕn'tūr), offer without being certain of success. (p. 131)

vic'tim (vĭk'tĭm), person or animal sacrificed, injured, captured, or destroyed. (p. 392)

Vi'kings (vī'kĭngz), Scandinavian explorers and sea-raiders. (p. 398)

vul'ner a ble (vŭl'nẽr ȧ b'l), capable of being wounded. (p. 201)

W

W.S.W., west-southwest on the compass. (p. 381)

waist'coat' (wās(t)'kōt'), vest. (p. 76)

wa'ter-por'ridge (wô'tẽr-pŏr'ĭj), a food made by boiling water and cereal. (p. 353)

Wil'liam Cul'len Bry'ant (wĭl'yăm kŭl'ĕn brī'ănt), American poet and journalist. (p. 375)

āte, ăm, câre, ȧsk, ȧbout, fär, bē, mĕt, hẽre, makẽr, bīte, bĭt, hōpe, hŏt, lôrd, ūse, ŭp, bûrn, thin, ~~then~~, pictūre, food, foot, out

ACKNOWLEDGMENTS

For permission to use copyrighted material, thanks are due the following publishers and authors:

D. Appleton-Century Company, for "Jack O' Lantern," from *I Have a Song to Sing You*, by Laura E. Richards.

Laura Benét and *Child Life*, for "Tom Pear-Tree"; and *Junior Red Cross News*, for "With a Barber's Brush."

Rosemary and Stephen Vincent Benét, for "Christopher Columbus," from *A Book of Americans*, published by Farrar & Rinehart, Inc. Copyright, 1933, by Rosemary and Stephen Vincent Benét.

Coward-McCann, Inc., and Ernest Benn, Ltd., for "Digging for Treasure," from *The Treasure Seekers*, by E. Nesbit.

E. P. Dutton & Co., Inc., for "The Wind and the Moon," from *The Poems of George Macdonald*.

Harcourt, Brace and Company, Inc., for "Mighty Mikko," from the collection of Finnish tales by that title by Parker Fillmore.

Harper & Brothers, for "The Christmas Promise," from *This Way to Christmas*, by Ruth Sawyer.

Henry Holt and Company, Inc., for "Five Eyes" and "The Ride-by-Nights," by Walter de la Mare.

Houghton Mifflin Company, for "The Plaint of the Camel," from *The Admiral's Caravan*, by Charles Edward Carryl; and "The Wagon in the Barn," from *All About Me*, by John Drinkwater.

Little, Brown & Company, for "The Lazy Water Carrier," from *Man's Long Climb*, by Marion F. Lansing.

Longmans, Green & Co., Inc., for "To Your Good Health," from *Crimson Fairy Book*, by Andrew Lang.

The Macmillan Company, for "Ashu and the Whirlwind," from *Girls in Africa*, by Erick Berry; "Fire," from *Fair American*, by Elizabeth Coatsworth; "For Christmas," from *The Pointed People*, by Rachel Field; "Dick Whittington's Cat," from *English Fairy Tales*, retold by Flora Annie Steel; and "The Shell," from *Collected Poems*, by James Stephens.

L. C. Page & Company, for "Phantom Cats," from *Stories of Little Animals*, by L. E. Mulets.

William R. Scott, Publishers, for the translation of the entries for October 10–12 from *The Log of Christopher Columbus' First Voyage to America*.

Frederick A. Stokes Company and William Blackwood & Sons, for "The Admiral's Ghost," from *Collected Poems, Volume II*, by Alfred Noyes.

Story Parade, for "The Last Snake," by Lavinia Davis; "Marathon," by Babette Deutsch; and "The Herring Cart," by Luis.

The Vanguard Press, for "Merry Tyll, the Jester," from *Tyll Ulenspiegel's Merry Pranks*, by M. Jagendorf.

Thanks are also due those authors who have permitted slight editing of their material for further ease in reading.